# Winning the Moon

Books by William Roy Shelton

COUNTDOWN
    THE STORY OF CAPE CANAVERAL

FLIGHTS OF THE ASTRONAUTS

AMERICAN SPACE EXPLORATION
    THE FIRST DECADE

SOVIET SPACE EXPLORATION
    THE FIRST DECADE

MAN'S CONQUEST OF SPACE

WINNING THE MOON

# Winning the Moon

by William Roy Shelton

*Illustrated by William Bradley*

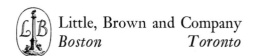

Little, Brown and Company
*Boston*　　　　*Toronto*

William R. Shelton gratefully acknowledges permission to quote from the
following source:

"Harold Urey, Adventurer," by William R. Shelton. *Science Year, The
World Book Science Annual.* Copyright © 1965 Field Enterprises Edu-
cational Corporation.

*For Toby*

# Acknowledgment

THIRTEEN YEARS AGO, when I covered space affairs for *Time* and *Life*, I took two guests to old Cape Canaveral for their first look at a rocket launch. One was Leslie Turner, for many years the distinguished magazine illustrator and comic strip artist for "Captain Easy and Wash Tubbs." The other was his lovely young daughter, Toby Turner.

In August of 1968, just prior to the four flights to the moon described in this book, I was reunited with the remarkable Turner family.

Today, as my wife, Toby has just expertly performed the hundred and one things not many people realize go into the preparation of a book of this type: finding and organizing information, transcribing notes often illegibly scribbled during the excitement of a rocket launch, typing letters and manuscripts, interviewing astronauts and scientists and spending countless hours in library research.

This was not why I married her, but the fact that she was able to do all this so willingly and well may be the main reason why reading about our flights to the moon could be nearly as pleasant an experience as writing about them.

W.R.S.

# Contents

# Winning the Moon

# 1

# The Target Moon

*What is there in thee, Moon! that thou shouldst move*
*My heart so potently?*

— JOHN KEATS, *Endymion*

"*Eagle's* TELEVISION CAMERA should be on soon. We should have a picture of Neil Armstrong any time now," the announcement came in over the loudspeaker. At 10:30 on the night of July 20, 1969, I felt lucky to have my son with me. I looked around the huge crowded auditorium at the Manned Spacecraft Center in Houston and noticed he was the only teen-ager present. The darkened room was filled with over a thousand members of the press. Many of them, like Mitsuaki Takao, the nervous Japanese journalist sitting beside me, had come from lands far away. An air of anxious expectancy hung over the room as all eyes remained fixed on two huge screens on the auditorium stage. Both screens, which would project a highly expensive television picture enlargement process, were dark and empty. Not a flicker of light crossed these strange and magic portholes which now for the first time existed as possible windows to the earth's past as well as, its future — and man's.

In my right pocket, warm from the heat of my body, I felt the small round object I had obtained at Cape Kennedy four days earlier, just after I had watched the magnificent launch of Apollo 11. The object was a bronze commemorative medal. On it were inscribed the words *Armstrong, Collins, Aldrin. First Manned Moon Landing.* I had gotten it to present to my son at the exact moment I was sure that man, an American man, had truly stepped down upon the virgin surface of our nearest neighbor in space.

Now, as a softly murmuring hush hung over the auditorium, that moment seemed just seconds away. In the stillness, as if from a great distance, I was suddenly startled to hear the words "Lord, stop by here" sung over and over like a deep-voiced chant. I was to learn later that the singing came from a Negro protest group sitting on the grass just outside the auditorium.

"We want them to land and come back safe," one of its members told me later, "but we want people to know also that here on earth right now are poor people who need food."

Inside the cavern of the darkened auditorium the words "Lord, stop by here" mumbled over and over from an unknown origin sounded like some strange and prayerful ritual from outer space. I felt my skin begin to tingle along the tops of my shoulders.

As we continued to wait before the enormous and still dark television windows, I glanced at my son. He was standing alone in the side aisle, his Nikon F camera held at the ready position in front of him, alert to get the first picture that came on the screen. Because of the size of the screen and expected quality of the picture, he had a chance to get an exceptionally good picture.

I studied him, and he seemed cool and professional. His face showed none of the excitement I felt at that moment. I concluded that for a nineteen-year-old Dana had had good training and preparation for the picture he was about to take. When he was only eight years old he had watched his first rocket rise from the old Cape Canaveral launch pads. He had stood barefoot on the white beach and shaded his eyes to watch the premiere flight of the mighty Atlas rocket. In the years since, while I reported space affairs for *Time*, *Life* and *Fortune* magazines, he had gotten to know many of the *Life* photographers who came to Florida. From some of them — especially Ralph Morse, Bob Kelley and Don Uhrbrock — he had acquired an abiding desire to become a journalistic photographer.

By the time he was sixteen, he had his first picture credit in a national magazine. In 1966, I had gone to Russia to interview Soviet cosmonauts and scientists and had brought back with me a colored window poster of Russian cosmonaut Valentina Tereshkova, the first woman in space, endorsing a wristwatch. He had shot a good black and white reproduction of this poster which was purchased by *Missiles and Rockets* magazine. It was through his skill with cameras, in fact, that now I was able to get him a pass into the working press area at the Manned Spacecraft Center. I studied his face as he waited calmly for what could be his most historic picture, and I felt he would get in his camera what he came after.

"Lord, stop by here," I heard again in the distance, and still the two huge screens remained dark.

Mitsuaki Takao suddenly asked, "You think the TV camera is going to work?"

"I don't know," I replied. "I sure hope so for all our sakes."

With no video before me, I tried to picture in my mind Neil Armstrong descending that ladder, completely encased in the layer upon layer of his $300,000 pressure suit.

I recalled an exciting afternoon in 1964 when I first got my hands on the remarkable pictures sent back to earth by the Ranger 7 lunar probe just before it crashed into the Sea of Clouds. A friend of mine at the Jet Propulsion Laboratory at Pasadena, California, had air-expressed a set of the close-up pictures to me in Houston so promptly that I received them even before they had appeared in newspapers. As soon as I saw the extraordinary quality of the pictures — the world's first historic close-up view of the moon — I put in a call to the Armstrong home in El Lago, a residential area not far from the Manned Spacecraft Center.

"Neil," I said, "I'm holding in my hand the first set of pictures just in from Pasadena. The quality is outstanding. They're great pictures. Would you like to see them?"

"You bet I would," he replied. "Come on over."

A few minutes later, when I arrived at the Armstrong home, Neil's wife Jan cleared off the kitchen table and I spread the fresh lunar pictures out for Neil to look at. He held each one carefully in his hands, examining it as if it were a priceless treasure, which indeed it was to a man who already dreamed of going to the moon.

"These are terrific," he said after a moment. "My first reaction is that the moon appears to have enough level places so we shouldn't have any trouble finding a safe landing spot. There are a lot of craters, but there're also a lot of level places in between."

"What about this deep layer of dust a lot of scientists have been claiming we will find?" I asked. "Some people have even said that the dust layer may be thick enough to swallow up the lunar lander."

"It just doesn't look like thick dust to me," Neil replied. "See the fairly sharp edges on these craters? If

*William Shelton and Neil Armstrong*

there were a lot of dust over them, I think the craters would be more rounded and less sharply defined. I think when the first man steps out on the moon his footprints will just barely sink into the surface."

For 1964, it was a good analysis and good prophecy. Neither one of us knew then, of course, that that first man would be Neil Armstrong himself. This was before any of the Apollo flights, and NASA officials were a long way from designating the crew for even the first Apollo flight, let alone the crew for the first lunar landing. And no one then knew, of course, whether or not the Russians would send a man to the moon before we would.

In the years after that, Neil had worked hard throughout the Gemini program and had impressed NASA officials with his enthusiasm, his alert mind, and his skill as a space pilot. Whenever he talked to me, or to anyone else, he never bothered to conceal the fact that he wanted to be the first man to set foot on the moon. Now, in July 1969, if everything continued to go well he was to have that chance.

"Lord, stop by here," I heard again.

Suddenly a lance of light shot across both screens. Dana's camera was up instantly, but I no longer watched him.

"We have a picture," the loudspeaker squawked.

A murmur of excitement and scattered cheers drowned out the chant, even though the picture at first made no sense. It was only an abstract pattern of light and dark. I leaned forward and squinted my eyes. Then I made out the pale, gray, rounded outline of Neil's left foot. The foot slowly descended from the lowest rung of

*Dana gets his picture*

the lunar module's ladder, and reached down tentatively like a tender finger exploring the heat of a candle flame. Then Neil withdrew his foot. When he put it down again, he put it down solidly and his right foot joined the first. We could see him now, a ghostly full figure standing in LEM's shadow. He looked for all the world like a fantastic snowman standing in the shadow of an earthly bridge.

"That's a small step for man, but a giant leap for mankind," * Neil Armstrong announced in his quiet, cool manner of speaking. It was the perfect symbolic and quotable statement. Instantly, the auditorium erupted in cheers. I heard yells, a woman screamed, then another. I glanced at Mitsuaki Takao; he was grinning delightedly.

During the next few minutes, as Neil explored and reported on the lunar territory immediately around LEM's base, three NASA men began moving down the aisles. They held large cardboard boxes and from them they passed out turquoise and white lapel buttons reading, LUNAR CONTACT. Dana, clutching one of the buttons in his hand and grinning broadly, came over to join me.

"I got the picture," he said. I reached in my pocket and drew out the warm bronze commemorative medal.

"Here's something I got for you at the Cape. I saved it until now, until I was absolutely sure that Neil was making footprints on the moon."

Since no other commemorative medals of the manned moon landing had been made available, Dana examined and fondled it as though it were precious metal from the moon itself.

All around us, reporters were racing off to their little curtained booths in the lobby to flash the first bulletins to newspapers all over the world. In many lands, giant presses had been sitting idle for hours, waiting for confirmation that the first man had indeed stepped out onto the surface of the moon.

---

* After returning to earth, Neil Armstrong explained that what he actually said was "That's a small step for a man . . ." The *a* however did not come through on the official NASA tapes.

The best of the TV pictures from the moon were still to come, but a highly symbolic step had been taken. A dream of ancient man, and a tantalizing and practical aspiration of twentieth-century man, had become a reality.

For me, the moment of Neil's first footprints on the moon transcended two earlier moments on Apollo 8 — the first manned circumlunar flight — that I thought would never be equaled. The flight of Apollo 8, we now realized, had been the "sleeper" flight of the Apollo series. Public interest had been so focused on the upcoming lunar landing that no one quite foresaw the emotional impact that would be generated by a manned flight that put three perceptive men in a seventy-mile-high orbit of the moon at Christmastime.

For that great event in late 1968, I had also been at the Manned Spacecraft Center press building in order to follow every detail of the flight of Frank Borman, Jim Lovell and Bill Anders. The first moment of taut drama came for me when these three men, the first two of whom I knew well, made their crucial lunar orbit insertion burn on the far side of the moon. We received no signal during this maneuver. The moon itself acted as a shield and a wall between earth and whatever fate was being enacted for Frank, Jim and Bill. When the unwitnessed and unrecorded time for the vital LOI burn came and went, there was no coffee break here on earth. The long silence at MSC was ponderable and profound. Did it fire? Did it fire correctly? We could only wait and hope.

While waiting, I reflected on the natures of the three-man crew. Bill Anders, whom I highly respected, I knew only slightly. But early in the Gemini program I had gotten to know Frank Borman when, with his help, I prepared an article titled, "You Don't Have to Be a Perfect Physical Specimen to Become an Astronaut." The article was based on all the physical infirmities Frank Borman had had to overcome to become an astronaut. Frank was completely candid with me as we wrote up the nearly incredible difficulties he had had earlier with a series of health problems. He laughingly told me that his medical problems had been further complicated when once he had been grounded for a suspected abdominal tumor that had showed up on X rays. It was later determined that the "tumor" was nothing more than congealed barium, the chalky fluid consumed like a vanilla milkshake as an aid to X-ray photography.

The next time I saw Frank after the article came out, he met me with a big grin.

"You have made me immortal," he said. "I now have identity. When people meet me they say, 'Oh, you're Frank Borman, the sick astronaut.'"

Jim and Marilyn Lovell had been one of my favorite astronaut couples since 1964. At that time I needed a place to dock a fast, 100-horsepower outboard ski boat I had just purchased from Gordon and Trudy Cooper. Jim and Marilyn, who had just bought a home on a placid canal leading into Taylor Lake, obligingly agreed that I could use their dock. For over a year, Jim used the boat during the week, while Dana and I took it out on weekends to take ski lessons from Trudy Cooper and her two attractive daughters Jan and Cam. It turned out that Jim Lovell knew more about mechanical aspects of the boat than I did and often helped me keep it running. He was invariably cheerful and patient; when something went wrong, he simply refused to be discouraged or give up until he had it fixed. This was precisely how he was later to react when the unexpected explosion in Apollo 13 almost brought a tragic end to that flight.

I knew that this same determination and optimism on Apollo 8 was now the welcome companion of Frank Borman and Bill Anders during their lonely and dangerous mission behind the moon. It seemed the longest time I had ever endured, waiting for Frank, Jim and Bill to emerge from behind the moon to tell us they were in a secure orbit.

The time for AOS (acquisition of signal) arrived, and no voice was heard.

Suddenly a small white light, called the DDD light, brightened on one of the key consoles.

"We've got it! We've got it!" the voice blared on the loudspeaker. And, almost simultaneously, I recognized Jim Lovell's voice reading out computer data.

When he finished his catalogue of essential data, Mission Control asked the precise question that was on everybody's mind: "What does the moon look like?"

"Okay, Houston," Jim said. "The moon is essentially gray, no color. Looks like plaster of Paris . . . The walls of the craters are terraced . . ."

I don't know which was the bigger thrill: knowing the crew was safe or hearing Lovell's — and man's — first description of the moon as it appeared just seventy miles below the lunar spaceship.

Jim, Frank and Bill continued to describe the moon as they swept over the moon's strange patina of circles, rip-

ples, sinuous rills and such exotic features as the Foaming
Sea, the crater Gutenberg, the Sea of Fertility and the
Pyrenees Mountains. "Like whitish-gray dirty beach
sand with lots of footprints in it," Bill Anders described
the moon's surface at one point.

The second most dramatic moment of the circumlunar
flight of Apollo 8 was at the end of the somewhat similar
behind-the-moon blackout that followed the critical
transearth insertion (TEI) burn designed to propel the
three men back to earth. Again there was no way of
knowing whether the burn failed, leaving them derelict
prisoners of the moon, or whether it worked to start
them home.

Again the DDD light; again Jim Lovell's voice:
"Houston," Jim happily announced, "please be informed
there is a Santa Claus . . . The burn was good."

But now, sitting in the MSC auditorium watching Neil
Armstrong's quietly efficient prospecting and Buzz Aldrin's wide-gaited, weirdly floating, shuffling, hopping,
jumping, kicking performance and scientific demonstration, I had to admit that my two personal high points of
the Apollo 8 mission had been surpassed.

For the first time, man was walking on a celestial body
other than his home planet. Future man, some had predicted, would one day construct new calendars — dating
not from the present year one, but from the day "mankind" took the first firm step on another solid object in
space.

During the time when the crew members of Apollo 11
were the moon's only inhabitants and, four months later,
when Pete Conrad and Alan Bean (Dick Gordon orbit-

ing) were there in Apollo 12, I went outside and stared at the crescent moon. Because I knew exactly how far they were from the moon's shadow line, or terminator, and because I knew they were on the lunar equator, I could pick out with my naked eye nearly the exact spot where they landed. The fact that men were there, as temporary inhabitants, made it like no other moon ever before beheld. Far from losing its mystery and its compelling magnetism, it had suddenly acquired a new and powerful allure. The moon was like a jewel or precious stone that one was about to receive or, reflecting from my childhood, like the biggest and most tempting package beneath the Christmas tree. What new questions — more intriguing even than the age-old questions — were we now about to ask? To me, that region of weirdly tilted and crater-pocked lunarscapes, that timeless region which had not changed its expression for a billion years, that untrampled surface of sublime desolation was now and forevermore the province of man.

## 2

# The Moon in Legend— the Impossible Dream

*There is no one among you, my brave colleagues, who has not seen the moon, or, at least, heard speak of it.*
— IMPEY BARBICANE,
In Jules Verne's *From the Earth to the Moon*, 1863

LET US CONSIDER the ancient moon. It is suspended in space, as if by magic, circling the earth once about every twenty-eight days. Even this fact, of course, was unknown to ancient man who knew neither that earth was a sphere nor that the moon was our natural satellite. From the beginning of life on earth, the moon has been the most dominant and magnetic object in the night skies. For centuries it has glowed with a strange and slowly creeping variable white light. It must truly have intrigued primitive man. Imagine some bushy-browed Neanderthal man squinting up at the full moon. What did he think, as he wrinkled his slanted forehead and rubbed his furry cheek in inquisitive speculation? Certainly, he thought of the moon as a friend. No harm came to him from it, and for roughly a quarter of his days, it lighted the limbs, vines, ladders, garbage heaps and foot-

*Primitive man*

smoothed earthen patios surrounding his primitive dwelling places. The moon enabled him to hunt and fish by night. And when he migrated, it lighted his trails, river courses and the broad sparkling expanses of the lakes and seas. The moon also was regular and reliable; he could tell time and count days by it.

Yet, despite its apparent friendliness, the moon also must have impressed primitive man with its ghostlike sense of silence and mystery. It was so tantalizingly close yet so remote that primitive man could touch it only in his fancy. What were the strange shapes and squiggles on its surface? Did other creatures live in its alternating dark and dazzling surface? Whence did it come? And what power did it have over the affairs of earth?

Other than a few crescent-shaped drawings on the walls of caves, no reliable record exists of how primitive man regarded our satellite. The oldest civilization from which records have passed down to us is that of the ancient Egyptians, who chose to believe that the moon rode in a boat as it moved across the sky. In the Louvre in Paris, an original stone statuette carved by the Egyptians depicts the protector of the boat, a moon god the Egyptians called Thoth. Thoth has the body of a man, the head of a curved-beaked bird, the ibis, and wears a crown depicting the upturned lunar crescent cradling a moonlike sphere, complete with craters. The ancient civilization of the Chinese made what Victor Hugo later called the "kingdom of dream, province of illusion" their patron of poetry. In the imaginative mythology of the ancient Greeks, the moon was the home of the beautiful goddess Diana, who also wore a crescent-shaped head-gear. Diana, sister of Helios, god of the sun, was also called Selene, a name that has survived in modern times in

*The Egyptian moon god Thoth*

the word selenography, which means the study of the surface features of the moon.

The temptation to make the moon prominent in man's myths, legends and superstitions continued down through the ages. It was the Romans who advanced the idea that anyone who exposed himself to what they called luna rays was risking ulcers, madness or even death. Hence our word lunatic, which originally meant moonstruck. In A.D. 100, when it was first noticed that the moon controlled the tides of earth's oceans, Plutarch said the moon was a second earth inhabited by demons living in caves. As late as the seventeenth century, the German astronomer Johannes Kepler repeated this theme in his view that the moon was inhabited by thick-skinned monsters who lived in caves to escape incineration by the sun. By then it was already the practice, and one still occasionally followed today, to plant certain crops, especially beans, when the moon's size is apparently increasing, or waxing. It was believed a waxing moon supplied energy to all living things, while a shrinking, or waning, moon was a time of dwindling life, or even death. Other superstitions maintained that ghosts walked during the full moon and that the dark moon was a time of evil deeds when the devil appeared on earth. To assure oneself of the best of luck, however, it was a good idea to carry a rabbit's foot taken by a cross-eyed person in a graveyard during the dark of the moon. Many believed the moon reddened at the time of the Crucifixion and that a "bloody" moon signified death. Among the weather prophets, there are still those who say that an upside-down crescent means that water is being poured from the "bowl" of the moon toward earth and that rain will soon fall.

The fanciful interpretation of the markings on the moon has also been a centuries-long preoccupation. Ancient Chinese interpreted these markings as the outline of a giant white hare. The man in the moon, in German legend, was sent there for stealing cabbages. French legend says the man in the moon is the banished Judas Iscariot, betrayer of Christ. In his *Divine Comedy*, the Italian Dante refers to the belief that the man in the moon is the Biblical Cain who slew his brother Abel. In the time of Captain James Cook, the simple and friendly island people of Tahiti in the South Pacific believed that white-winged doves had carried seeds of fruit trees to the moon, and that the moon's dark splotches were tranquil

*Doves of Tahitian legend*

groves of trees. Two centuries ago, the American Chero-
kee Indians thought the man in the moon was actually an
old woman seated with a cat and a bowl of hominy at her
feet as she spliced her warrior's headband.

To others, the bright moon has always stimulated love
and signified romance. To many a songwriter, the fact
that "moon" rhymes with "June" and "soon" has been
an irresistible temptation. They have sung the praises of
the Christmas moon, the South Pacific moon, the Ne-
braska moon, the moon over Miami, and the harvest
moon, which is still an actual visual aid and blessing at
crop-gathering times all over the world. Poets of various
degrees of talent have often praised what Percy Bysshe
Shelley called "that orbèd maiden, with white fire laden,
whom mortals call the Moon." The poet John Keats

once asked, "What is there in thee, moon, that thou shouldst move my heart so potently?" The story is told that on England's bleak northeast coast, the children of fishermen still chant, "I see the moon and the moon sees me. God bless the sailors on the sea." William Shakespeare once put the following words into Hotspur's mouth: "By heaven methinks it were an easy leap To pluck bright honor from the pale-fac'd moon."

The mission of Apollo, of course, was to do much more than to "pluck bright honor" from the conquest of the moon, although honor, prestige and pride were all natural consequences of the initial landings. As we shall see later in this book, our reasons for going to the moon were a combination of many factors: evolutionary curiosity, intellectual curiosity, and the compelling desire, ingrained in all civilizations, to find out where we came from and how the earth, the moon and the solar system originated. The only thing different about modern man is that he alone, of all men who have lived on earth, has had the means, through sophisticated technology, of getting there.

Until the mid-seventeenth century, even the most learned men believed that the air we breathed on earth extended all the way to the moon. Such a belief accounts for some of the bizarre methods of earth-moon locomotion used in early legends and in later science-fiction accounts of space travel. If a man wanted to go to the moon, many believed, he could go on wearing his normal attire as he worked and ate his way through the friendly ocean of air. After all, to many imaginers of such a grand adventure the moon looked reasonably close, especially on a clear winter night when, with the naked eye alone, they could pick out mountains and valleys along the lunar shadow line. A trip to the moon was mainly a question of taking along enough food and, of course, selecting a suitable propulsion system.

Before the age of modern science, however, even such rudimentary considerations as food and distance seemed not to matter to storytellers. Greek mythology, for instance, provides us with the familiar journey of Icarus, not to the near moon but to the remote sun. Icarus's father Daedalus made his son wings of feathers and wax, then watched in horror as Icarus flew so close to the sun that its heat melted the wax and Icarus plunged to his death in the Agean Sea. In an account written by the first known science-fiction writer, a Syrian named Lucian of Samos, sailors of the second century were blown to the moon by a whirlwind. But Lucian knew, even then, that his journey was not solidly based on scientific fact.

"So all readers beware," he wrote in his introduction. "Don't believe a word of it."

Other early accounts relied on such strange means of earth-moon locomotion as chariots and even swans and geese. In the seventeenth century, writer-soldier Cyrano de Bergerac in *Voyages to the Moon and Sun* first used the then current belief that the morning sun causes the dew to rise. De Bergerac had his first astronaut rise by attaching bottles of dew to his body. Another would-be "lunarnaut" greased his body with beef marrow because, de Bergerac wrote, "I knew that at the time the moon was waning and that during this quarter she is wont to suck up the marrow of animals." Later, de Bergerac hit it right: he invented a machine powered by a series of rockets. But in that same century, Germany's Johannes Kepler wrote of such unscientific devices as demons which ferried people to the moon during an eclipse.

*A moon flight using Cavorite*

Even Jules Verne, who consulted with his science-trained brother, used a 900-foot-long cannon to propel his passengers *From the Earth to the Moon* in 1863. Not even the tremendous forces of acceleration resulting from the cannon's blast which would have scrambled his passengers' brains deterred him. In *The First Man on the Moon*, written by H. G. Wells, in the early twentieth century, the author invented a fictitious substance we would certainly welcome today. Indeed, many people are still looking for it. Called Cavorite, Wells's substance defied gravity and was applied as coating around a sphere. All the space pilots inside the sphere had to do was open a window aimed at the moon and the moon would draw the sphere toward it. Simplicity itself! And not an ounce of fuel! If one wanted to amass a fortune, the discovery of a real Cavorite would do the job quite nicely; it would not only revolutionize space travel, it would also solve the commuter and traffic problem, run elevators, and perform other services now unimaginable.

But as Chapter 3 discusses, it was real events, not fictional accounts, that made the vital deposits in the bank of men's knowledge of the real nature of travel to the moon.

# 3

# How to Get There— the Possible Dream

*The earth is the cradle of humanity, but mankind will not stay in the cradle forever.*

— KONSTANTIN TSIOLKOVSKY,
Russia's "Father of Rocketry"

AMONG THE REAL EVENTS which made possible the Apollo flights to the moon were high-altitude balloon experiments that began about 1800. A Frenchman named J. L. Gay-Lussac in 1804 rode a balloon to 23,000 feet where he recorded subzero temperatures. An Englishman, James Glaisher, blacked out at 29,000 feet in 1862. A few years later, the first deaths attributed to high altitude occurred when two French balloonists died of oxygen starvation at 27,950 feet. Thus, man proved the hard way that the insulation and nourishment of earth's friendly air is lost within just a few miles of the earth's surface. Observing this phenomenon, Auguste Piccard of Switzerland told himself that he would build a sealed cabin and take earth's air with him. When in 1931 Piccard safely rose 52,000 feet in his airtight cabin, he had, in effect, designed a rudimentary spacecraft.

As the age of aviation evolved, man refined his methods of high-altitude survival. At first, in open-air cockpits, he just wore warmer clothing. Then he fed oxygen to his body through a face mask. Finally, he enclosed and pressurized the cabin of his aircraft, warmed it with heaters and cooled it with air conditioners. In less than two decades man has added other refinements: ice for his drinks, heat for his meals and a comfortable bathroom. Through these improvements, man's efforts toward atmospheric controls and his ability to "package" a part of earth's environment and take it with him provided the technological prerequisites for the spacecraft of the immediate future.

But balloons and powered aircraft were helpless beyond the thin halo of earth's atmosphere.

Before Yuri Gagarin's breakthrough space flight of October 4, 1957, the highest man had gone in balloons was 13.71 miles and the aircraft altitude record held by the X-15 rocket plane was under twenty miles. That is less than one twelve-thousandth of the approximately 242,000 miles distance to the moon. To find out the unknowns that lay thirty miles high and beyond, another means of providing and sustaining lift was needed. For this, man had to await the development of the rocket motor, possibly the most important and enduring means of transportation ever devised on earth.

Man's knowledge of the principles of rocket propulsion has its roots in ancient history, much of it military history. Anyone who has ever seen a firecracker fizzle instead of explode, and propel itself across the sidewalk spewing smoke, has witnessed a perfect example of

*Three types of flying suits*

rocket propulsion obtained by the burning of solids. Firecrackers as used by the ancient Chinese preceded the invention of gunpowder. In 360 B.C., a Greek who called himself Archytas of Tarentum built a small, hollow wooden dove which he suspended on stout threads like a marionette. Inside the dove, he placed a small cylinder of

compressed steam. When the steam was expelled to the
rear, it provided the first known example of jet propulsion as the suspended dove sped in circles. Delighted
Greeks witnessed a primitive but significant experiment.
In a basic rocket engine, the escape of expanding gases
from a confined space provides an "action." The "reaction" of the gas container is to move in the opposite direction. Although it was not realized for many years, the
fact that this "action-reaction" works best in the friction-
less and airless void of a vacuum made it the ideal propulsion system for travel in space.

The first applications of this theory, of course, were in
the atmosphere. The flaming rockets first used by the
Chinese against their enemies the Mongols were called
"arrows of flying fire," and were not too unlike present-
day Christmas "sky rockets." Gunpowder rockets, however, were not very efficient nor accurate, so they had to
be used in clusters. Ancient literature records the fact
that such primitive missiles cascaded toward the enemy
"on a solid front like one hundred tigers."

Over a period of several centuries, some of the new
rocket weapons moved down the long caravan routes to
Europe. Europeans called them "the casing that flies"
and used them at first in fireworks displays. By the 1800s,
however, rockets were seeing prominent use as artillery
weapons. In 1807, a British colonel, William Congreve,
launched thousands of rockets weighing about thirty
pounds each against Copenhagen in the War of the
Third Coalition, which was a part of the Napoleonic
Wars between England and France. A few years later, in
the War of 1812, the British used similar rockets against

Fort McHenry in Baltimore, Maryland. It was this bombardment that writer Francis Scott Key was later to immortalize with the words "the rocket's red glare" in the National Anthem of the United States, "The Star-Spangled Banner."

By World War I, conventional artillery had improved so much that military rockets saw only limited use in launching flares and command signals. A few of the famous French Nieuport biplanes fired airborne rockets which were meant to ignite the hydrogen-filled observation balloons used by the Germans. The men who bailed out to escape the rocket-ignited hydrogen were the first men to use parachutes. A few rockets were also fired from the ground at German Zeppelins.

Until this time, all military rockets employed were "solid" rockets which achieved thrust by the simple but unreliable and unthrottleable burning of derivatives of gunpowder. But on both sides of the Atlantic, a handful of imaginative men, already dreaming of a rocket to the moon, began to experiment with a true rocket motor using liquid propellant as fuel. The first of these was a nearly deaf Russian dreamer who was practical enough, as the Russians say, to "put rivets in his dreams." His name was Konstantin Eduardovich Tsiolkovsky.

Tsiolkovsky, who was born in 1857, died in 1935. When I visited the Soviet Union in 1966, one of my purposes was to visit his former home and workshop in Kaluga, some 125 miles from Moscow.

During the long drive in a little Volga car, I saw several evidences of the space age, including Sputnik (which means "satellite" in Russian), drawings and symbols on road signs. But, in contrast to the mechanical marvel of Sputnik, the world's first artificial satellite, I also saw many Russian trucks and motorcycles broken-down on the highways. Only once did I see a filling station and never a garage. On my first visit to what will surely become one of the world's foremost shrines to honor the birth of the space age, this mechanical contrast between the precision of space hardware and the defects of earthbound vehicles seemed odd.

When I arrived in Kaluga with my interpreter, Soviet editor Yevgeni Ruzhnikov, we were met by a Tass reporter and Tsiolkovsky's grandson, Alexei Konstin, a studious-looking, bespectacled man of about thirty.

As the first American writer to visit the river city of Kaluga, I was accorded unusual curiosity and attention. The Kaluga newspaper, which was very proud of Tsiolkovsky's role as the Soviet "Father of Rocketry," even ran a front-page story on the fact that an American had come a great distance to see where Tsiolkovsky had lived and worked. My host, Alexei Konstin, was at first somewhat cool and aloof. An incident occurred, however, which caused him to warm up noticeably. With the help of a science attaché named Boris Romanoff in the Soviet Embassy in Washington, I had been able to read prior to my visit everything that had ever been translated into English about Tsiolkovsky and his work. I had even memorized some of his numerous sayings and prophecies. When the translator started to interpret Alexei's descriptions of a Tsiolkovsky inscription cut into a stone monument in Kaluga park, I surprised Alexei and the interpreter by quoting the rest of the inscription from memory: "Man will not stay on earth forever, but in the pursuit of life and space will first emerge timidly from the bonds of the atmosphere and then advance until he has conquered the whole of circumsolar space."

Alexei Konstin broke into a big smile. From that point forward, he was my friend and spent long hours interpreting his famous grandfather's genius and vision. Alexei showed me Tsiolkovsky's workbench which he had pushed into town one winter by turning it upside down and using it as a sled. On top of the workbench was what Tsiolkovsky called "one of my inventions that really worked," an old-fashioned tin ear trumpet he used because of his deafness. It looked much like a tin funnel.

Downstairs in the small frame house were various models of rockets and rocket motors Tsiolkovsky had worked on, plus his early conception of a dirigible, an all-metal, cigar-shaped "bag" which he called an aerostat. Upstairs was the inventor's bedroom which was connected to a sloping roof by what Tsiolkovsky's family referred to as "the doorway to the stars." In his later years, the old man was fond of walking through that doorway in the evenings to spend long hours standing on the roof studying the moon and stars, dreaming of space travel.

Even as a youth, according to Alexei, Tsiolkovsky constantly dreamed about space travel. This was especially true after he reached the age of nine, when an attack of scarlet fever rendered him almost totally deaf. His affliction caused his mind to turn inward to the world of dreams.

"In my imagination," Tsiolkovsky later wrote of his

childhood, "I could jump higher than anybody else, could climb poles like a cat and walk ropes. I dreamed there was no such thing as gravity."

He also studied hard, especially mathematics and physics, and he constructed all kinds of objects ranging from tissue paper balloons to primitive range finders, or devices for judging distance. Shortly after his parents sent him, at sixteen, to study in Moscow, the idea of conquering space came to him very strongly. Like many people who are young and full of enthusiasm, his first inspired "invention" appeared to solve the problem all at once. He imagined a wooden box that contained two steel balls attached to the tops of two flexible metal rods. His plan was to rotate the two balls rapidly, thus creating centrifugal force that would, he thought, cause the box to rise all the way to the moon.

"My heart still swells," he wrote later, "with the exultation I experienced on that unforgettable night." He wandered the streets of Moscow all night long, he recalled, "thinking of the grave consequences of my invention." In the cold light of dawn, however, he finally had to admit to himself that it simply would not work out the way he thought it would.

"From that moment," he wrote, "the idea of space flight never left my mind."

He received his first recognition, at the age of twenty-four, for a scientific paper he wrote titled "Free Space." Thereafter, he alternated between work on space theory, including science-fiction accounts of space travel, and the construction of models of dirigibles, wind tunnels, single-winged airplanes and rockets.

He always had a vision: "to place one's feet on the soil of asteroids, to lift a stone from the moon with your hand, to construct moving stations in ether space . . . to observe Mars at a distance of several tens of miles."

In some of his science-fiction accounts, his imagination ran wild, sometimes with astonishing accuracy. In his book *On the Moon*, he visualized himself and another man waking up in their own house on the lunar surface.

"When we wanted to move rapidly," he wrote, almost as Buzz Aldrin might have described it, "we had to lean perceptibly forward like a horse when starting to pull a heavy cart . . . Every movement we made was exceedingly light . . . We learned to move by leaps and bounds . . . In short, by force of circumstances, we were transformed into jumping animals, like grasshoppers and frogs."

In one other aspect, he was also accurately prophetic. From the moon, he said, "neither stars nor planets twinkled, which made them like silver-capped nails studding the black firmament."

Aside from his dreams, visions and prophecies, Tsiolkovsky's long life produced concrete applications to both the theory and mechanics of space flight. He modeled one of the first true liquid-propellant rocket motors, employing kerosene and liquid oxygen (propellants widely used today) and a system for cooling the rocket chamber by the flow of propellants around the combustion chamber, a process we call curtain cooling today. He foresaw the use of space suits, the mooring of people and objects in the weightless state, the closed ecological system — a food-producing space garden which feeds on waste products — and rendezvous and docking.

He was not without fame, recognition and financial assistance in Russia. On his seventy-fifth birthday, Stalin himself sent him a telegram of congratulations. By the time of his death in 1935, although few people, even Russians, were yet convinced that the world was on the eve of the age of space, Konstantin Tsiolkovsky was both a popular and a scientific hero in his homeland. One of his students and admirers was a young rocket enthusiast, Friedrick Tsander, who became so enthralled over the idea of space travel that he later named both his children after stars. It was a Tsander-designed brass and aluminum rocket, eighteen inches long, that rose from a wooded area near Moscow on November 25, 1933, and burned for eighteen seconds. But Tsiolkovsky's protégé was not able to witness those few historic seconds; he was already dying in a nearby sanatorium.

Two other countries, Germany and the United States, also had early experimenters and spokesmen in the cause of rocket flight. In Germany, Professor Hermann Oberth wrote a book in 1923 that was to become the bible of German rocketeers, *The Rocket into Interplanetary Space*. Stimulated by Oberth, a German group four years later formed the now famous VER, Society for Space Travel, at Breslau, Germany.

I have met Professor Oberth only twice. The first time was in 1959, when the United States Army flew him for the first time to see the launch pads at old Cape Canaveral. Oberth was then sixty-five, and it was not his words so much as the expression in his eyes that told me how often he had dreamed of the sight he was then witnessing: the row of great rocket gantries lined up along the wide Atlantic beach, all of them aimed at the same cosmos that had preoccupied our distinguished visitor from Germany for all of his life. I did not see the aging professor again until the 1969 launch of Apollo 11 from pad 39A at the much more modern Kennedy Space Center. Officials had thoughtfully flown Oberth to the site so he could see the launch of the rocket that was to place the first men on the moon. He was a pensive onlooker whose countenance seemed to suggest that he had seen it all before in the obsessed eye of the mind.

"You kindled the fire," Oberth once wrote Konstantin Tsiolkovsky, "we shall not let it die; we shall try to realize man's greatest dream."

In helping to realize that dream, Oberth was also influenced by the science-fiction writers.

"At the age of eleven," he wrote, "I received from my mother as a gift the famous Jules Verne books, which I read at least five or six times and, finally, knew by heart."

During World War I, he proposed long-range, liquid-propelled guided missiles to the German War Department, but his concept was rejected. He continued to work on rockets and in his book of 1923, he formulated plans for a sophisticated liquid-fueled rocket to take soundings of the upper atmosphere. By 1929, he had published a second book, *The Road to Space Travel*, and was also president of the Society for Space Travel.

All during the 1920s, German youths became fascinated with model rockets, partly because of Oberth's attempt to launch a rocket for a German movie. When Oberth's rocket failed to fire, nearly every youth in Germany thought he could build one that would work.

In the 1930s, Oberth's society moved to the Kummersdorf airfield near Berlin. There Oberth, an army captain named Walter Dornberger, and a young and enthusiastic technician named Wernher von Braun expanded their ranks to over a hundred persons. With modest funds from the army, they had fired two liquid rockets to an altitude of 6,500 feet by the mid-1930s.

But the first firing of a liquid-propelled rocket was not a German feat. In the late 1920s, Oberth — and, indeed, all rocketeers then in Europe — had heard of the American Dr. Robert Hutchings Goddard (1882–1945), who had fired the first liquid-propelled rocket in 1926. Oberth had written to Goddard after reading a newspaper account of his rocket flight. Oberth suggested to Goddard, as he did to Tsiolkovsky, that they exchange their theories and data. Wrote Professor Oberth to Professor Goddard, "I think that only by the common work of scholars of all nations can be solved this great problem . . . to pass over the atmosphere of earth by means of a rocket."

Robert Goddard had actually begun to think about this same problem just after the turn of the century while he was in high school at his home in Worcester, Massachusetts. He was highly stimulated by reading Jules Verne's account of a trip to the moon and also had read H. G. Wells's *War of the Worlds*. By the time Goddard received his doctorate degree from Clark University in Worcester, he had discovered, quite independently of Tsiolkovsky, that liquid oxygen was the best "oxidizer" in the combustion of liquid propellants such as kerosene and liquid hydrogen. Even compared to Tsiolkovsky, Goddard was remarkably advanced in his theories of rocket flight. Thankfully, he was the kind of man who wasn't satisfied with theories and plans. At a comparatively early age, he started to mix various kinds of fuels and to build rudimentary rockets with his own hands to see if what made sense on paper would work on a firing range. By the age of twenty-nine, he was already lecturing on ways to get to the moon. At thirty-four, he submitted a paper entitled "A Method of Reaching Extreme Altitudes" to the Smithsonian Institution in Washington. He received a $5,000 grant from the Institution to conduct rocket research, but later, when some newspapers got a copy of his paper, their writers ridiculed him. Somewhat incidentally, Goddard had suggested that men on earth could tell when a rocket hit the moon by its discharge of a flash powder explosion at the instant of impact. Newspapers pooh-poohed this idea. One paper wrote that the man who made such a proposal lacked even the knowledge "daily ladled out in high schools."

After Goddard actually began to fire small rockets from his Aunt Effie's farm outside Auburn, Massachusetts, the criticism, including that of nearby residents, increased. In 1929, after one rocket exploded just after launch, police, reporters and ambulances descended on the scene. One newspaper headlined, MOON ROCKET MISSES TARGET BY 238,799½ MILES. Others called him

"Moony" Goddard, and he was forced to move his experiments elsewhere.

Four years later, from the sands of Roswell, New Mexico, an eighty-five-pound rocket he named Nell rose 7,500 feet and reached nearly the speed of sound. Nell contained a pressurized oxygen tank, a self-cooling combustion chamber and a gyroscope and was the forerunner and prototype of all liquid-propelled rockets that have been fired since.

By now Goddard was finally attracting serious attention. Even the nation's number one hero, Colonel Charles A. Lindbergh, who in 1927 had become the first man to fly the Atlantic, offered to help him. Lindbergh was influential in getting Goddard a grant of fifty thousand dollars from his good friend and philanthropist Daniel Guggenheim.

When World War II began in 1939, no one realized that Robert Goddard and his small crew of rocket helpers, including his wife Esther, knew more about rockets than anyone else in the world. They had constructed such advanced rockets that in 1950 when Wernher von Braun examined the shy professor's list of over two hundred rocket patents for the first time he exclaimed, "Goddard was ahead of us all."

But the United States Government made surprisingly little use of either Robert Goddard's patiently conceived theories or his brilliantly constructed high-altitude rockets, asking him only to help in the development of a rocket device to assist World War II airplanes on takeoff.

As the world now knows, Hermann Oberth, Walter

Dornberger and Wernher von Braun in Germany received no such neglect. As World War II approached, the group of dedicated rocketmen who had been working at Kummersdorf moved to a new secret rocket base called Peenemünde on the windswept coast of the Baltic Sea. Here, under the impetus of Hitler's dream of world conquest, their funds swelled and their numbers multiplied.

In the spring of 1944, near the end of World War II, a curious object came out of the sky over Sweden and crashed in a field. Those who examined its twisted remains had no way of knowing that it was the first of one of the deadliest weapons ever devised for warfare. It was so new, so rare, and so unexpected that there was no known defense against it. What had accidentally landed on Swedish soil was the final product of all the creative energy, drive, and hard work that had been expended at Peenemünde: the first of the dreaded V–2 "wonder weapons."

Three months later the rain of V–2 rockets began on England and Antwerp, Belgium, then held by the allies. The V–2 was a true ballistic rocket, and at 46.2 feet in length and 5.4 feet in diameter, it was the largest mass-produced rocket ever constructed. Propellants were 75 percent alcohol, plus liquid oxygen. At takeoff, it weighed 28,500 pounds and could develop 56,000 pounds of thrust for 65 seconds, enough to send it 3,600 miles per hour and 60 miles high. After engine cutoff, the V–2 coasted all the rest of the way to the target in a ballistic trajectory — that is, on a course like that of an artillery shell. When it hit the ground, its deadly 2,200-pound warhead exploded with devastating effect.

If the V-2's had appeared just one year earlier, they could well have reversed the outcome of the war in Europe. Despite repeated attacks of RAF bombers on Peenemünde, where their bombs sometimes exploded in wet concrete so urgent was the pace of construction, and despite United States Army Air Corps and Navy attacks on suspected V-2 factories and launch sites, one factory alone continued to produce over three hundred V-2's per month, according to an estimate by von Braun. At war's end, over three thousand V-2's had bombarded London alone.

What happened to all this highly advanced rocketry at the end of World War II? Both Russia and the United States captured many separate V-2 rockets that were to be patiently taken apart, analyzed, put back together again and fired. This hardware in itself was a priceless booty of war. But the real booty was the brainpower that had used the principles of Tsiolkovsky, Oberth and Goddard to create the first large practical rocket capable of leaving earth's atmosphere. And this brainpower, with very few exceptions, came to the United States.

As the advancing Russians approached Peenemünde, technical director Wernher von Braun called his staff together.

"This is important," he told them. "We will carry our administration and structure straight across Germany. This will not be a rout."

According to one of the Peenemünde Germans, Dieter

*Goddard, von Braun and Tsiolkovsky*

Huzel, who wrote the fascinating book *Peenemünde to Canaveral*, there was no doubt in anyone's mind that when they surrendered, they would surrender to the Americans, not to the Russians. This was the reason von Braun chose to move the entire group westward toward the advancing Americans.

Von Braun had all the most important blueprints, some of them for truly tremendous rockets, and other key documents and plans carefully packed in five German Army trucks. The elite SS troops were then dealing severely with any Germans who showed even the slightest inclination not to fight to the death, so von Braun forged a set of orders for the unusual convoy in order to conceal the true nature of the highly valuable cargo from Hitler's troops.

Dieter Huzel, who now lives in California and whom I have since learned to know as a friend and fellow correspondent, was put in charge of the trucks. He knew well the unusual significance of his dangerous journey westward.

"Those documents," Huzel wrote, "were of inestimable value. Whoever inherited them would be able to start in rocketry at that point at which we had left off, with the benefits not only of our accomplishments, but of our mistakes as well — the real ingredients of experience. They represented years of intensive effort in a brand new technology, one that, all of us were still convinced, would play a profound role in the future course of human events."

After many delays and narrow escapes, Huzel led what he called his "cache of scientific documents unlike any in history" westward. Finally, in the Harz Mountains of southwestern Germany, near the town of Dörnten, he found a secluded cave. There, in great secrecy, he unloaded his five trucks, stored his cargo inside the cave, then dynamited the cave entrance. Temporarily, at least, the greatest secrets of the entire German military effort lay mute and dark beneath the surface of the earth — like some ancient cache of arrowheads.

It was a long time before von Braun and his group of rocket "brains" found American officers knowledgeable

enough about rocketry to realize what was being offered
them in exchange for the privilege of the group's continuing to work on rockets, on the attempt to orbit earth
satellites, and on rockets to the moon and planets.
Finally, a United States Army officer named Colonel
H. N. Toftoy realized the significance of what was
in their brains and inside the dynamited entrance to
Dieter Huzel's secret cave. When the cave was finally
blasted open, its invaluable contents were shipped
straight to the army's Aberdeen Proving Grounds in
Maryland.

On a dull rainy afternoon of May 2, 1945, Dieter Huzel, Wernher von Braun, Wernher's brother Magnus
von Braun, General Dr. Walter Dornberger and three
other key Peenemünde veterans became the first of over
a hundred German rocket experts to begin the long journey to the United States. As the seven men climbed into
U. S. Army vehicles, Huzel later wrote: "Everyone was
serious, thoughtful, silent. No one knew what the future
held, either in the next few moments in Schattwals, or in
the days, months, and years that might follow . . . I
had the uneasy sensation that this was now all that remained of one of the greatest engineering adventures of
modern times."

He was wrong, of course. The now possible dream of
Tsiolkovsky, Oberth and Goddard, the now possible
dream of those silent men heading for America and the
now possible dream of a handful of American rocketmen
were all to be joined in the future to undertake incredible
ventures. Within a quarter of a century, the deadly new

arrows of war would be enlarged beyond even the most ambitious Peenemünde blueprint in order to fashion a rocket to the moon. It was to be a great rocket that not even Jules Verne or H. G. Wells could have imagined.

# 4

# The Great Escape

*. . . not because [it] will be easy, but because it will be hard — because [it] will serve to organize and measure the best of our energies and skills — because that challenge is one we are willing to accept, one we are unwilling to postpone.*

— PRESIDENT JOHN F. KENNEDY,
September 12, 1962, in commenting
on the plan to send men to the moon

THE MOOD OF FRUSTRATION that Peenemünde veteran Dieter Huzel felt at the end of World War II was to continue for several years. The Peenemünde group of about 125 Germans were given a five-year contract with the United States Army and were shipped to the remote Southwestern desert area near Fort Bliss, Texas.

Once in Huntsville, Alabama, where the Germans were eventually moved, I asked a Peenemünde veteran named Walter Weisman what they did at Fort Bliss during their first five-year contract. His answer reflected the impatience that arose in them from prolonged inactivity:

"We taught each other English, played chess and occasionally chased empty V–2 fuel tanks which the wind blew across the desert like tumbleweeds. Von Braun wrote a book on a space trip to Mars. All of us were frustrated. We were itching to get on with larger rockets and put an earth satellite into orbit."

In contrast, rocketmen in the Soviet Union were working full speed to launch the world's first artificial satellite. The Russians had taken hundreds of captured V–2's to their own secret firing ranges and, with the assistance of captured German rocketmen and a handful of Peenemünde veterans who had elected to surrender to the Russians, they quickly mastered the V–2 secrets. When I visited the Soviet Union in 1966, I found abundant evidence that the Russians wasted little time in expanding the basic V–2 into truly large rockets that were eventually capable of lifting record-breaking payloads of all types.

On our side of the Atlantic it was a full decade after the end of World War II before the Peenemünde veterans and the United States Army developed the short-range but highly reliable Redstone rocket. In the old days at Cape Canaveral, whenever I wanted to show one of my visiting friends a rocket launch I always picked a Redstone because, of all our early rockets, it was the only one regularly to be launched on time. In the mid-fifties, I frequently watched the launches of the air-breathing, aerodynamic Snarks, Matadors and Bomarcs and the medium-range Navaho, Thor and Jupiter rockets, but these required long hours, and sometimes days, of patient waiting in the sand dunes surrounding the Cape. I never saw a Redstone explode, but all of the other early rockets at one time or another blew up before our eyes in great billowing explosions that smelled ominously of ozone and burnt kerosene. Dieter Huzel had said, however, that in rocketry you learn as much from failures as from successes.

One October day in 1957, I was sitting in my home near Cape Canaveral watching the New York Yankees play the Milwaukee Braves in the televised World Series when a startling announcement came over the air. The Russians, the announcement said, had just launched the first artificial earth satellite. I jumped in my MG TF–1500 and raced to the Starlite Motel, which was a favorite hangout for off-duty rocketmen. They were all watching the World Series, too. Few of my friends then showed the profound disappointment that was soon to characterize the American reaction to the launch of the early Sputniks.

Orbiting an artificial satellite, we now know, was the first practical step taken in the direction of the beckoning moon. Both Russia and the United States were later to use a "parking" orbit as the first step in the journey to the moon. By the time Russia launched Sputniks 2 and 3, in rapid order, American alarm had grown to epic proportions.

Our national pride received still another severe jolt the cold morning of December 6, 1957. From the damp and chilly sands of Cocoa Beach, newsmen and photographers watched and recorded the explosion of our Vanguard rocket as it attempted to orbit the first U.S. satellite. We saw the fireball of the exploding rocket rise from the pad like a violently burning balloon. Engineers inside the Vanguard blockhouse felt the explosion, then saw the interior concrete walls reflect red through the periscope windows.

As word of the failure of our first satellite spread to a waiting nation, the initial reaction was that we had suffered a humiliating defeat.

"Overnight," wrote Wernher von Braun, who was now an American citizen, "it became popular to question the bulwarks of our society; our public education system, our industrial strength, international policy, defense strategy and forces, the capability of our science and technology. Even the moral fiber of our people came under searching examination."

Actually, of course, the conspicuous failure of Vanguard focused the attention of the public and of Congress on our second-rate position in the new science of astronautics. In the long run, this attention, and the long postponed funds that went with it, gave our space program a needed shot in the arm.

National aspirations and attention now shifted to the Peenemünde veterans who, on November 7, 1957, had finally been authorized to try to launch an earth satellite. On that date, a determined and confident Wernher von Braun promised Congress that he and the U. S. Army would put a satellite into orbit within three months.

On the night of January 31, 1958, the press was allowed inside the Cape to see it happen. From the Cape's first press site about a mile from the big Jupiter C booster, we watched in fascination as the miracle rocket spurted fire. As it moved upward into the night sky, a nation's hopes went with it. When the 18.13-pound satellite, which spun like a rifle bullet, went firmly into orbit, these hopes turned into jubilation and pride. A month and a half later, a new and improved Vanguard put our second satellite into orbit.

The United States did not know it at the time, but it was already launched on its journey to the moon.

In October of that same year, the new National Aeronautics and Space Administration began operations. Von Braun and his Huntsville, Alabama team, now augmented by over four thousand American rocketmen, were turned over to NASA along with over $100 million in rocket equipment and blueprints, including the detailed plans for the Saturn 1 rocket.

NASA's programs included everything from aviation research and development to the construction of meteorological and other scientific satellites, but its initial directive to orbit a living human being was the aspect of space exploration that received the most attention. It is important to remember that prior to this directive, scarcely a man in America, scientist, engineer or laymen, thought that anyone could possibly send a man into space for at least ten years.

Yet on April 12, 1961, a day now celebrated as Cosmonaut Day in the Soviet Union, Russia sent a shy cosmonaut named Yuri Alekseyevich Gagarin once around the earth. And when I flew into the Cape late that evening, I could see extensive preparations already underway for the forthcoming suborbital flight of astronaut Alan B. Shepard. Three weeks later, we saw the Mercury–Redstone rocket standing in a dawn mist like a spectral candle. As the sun rose over the Atlantic, the horizontal

*Shepard, Grissom and Glenn*

wraiths of mist turned into magnificently hued bands of
rosy gold that weirdly lifted and settled as the ground
warmed.

Then the unbelievable blast-off with a living, breathing man in the nose began.

"This is seven," Alan Shepard announced. "Fuel is go
. . . and the oxygen is go."

The nation was also go, as Freedom 7 pierced the

*President John F. Kennedy*

clouds and, nearly a minute later, emerged, smaller and serenely climbing into a successful 302-mile flight.

Two months later, we saw Gus Grissom take off on a similar fifteen-minute suborbital ride through the blanket of our atmosphere. Then, in February 1962, a personable, smiling Marine colonel named John Herschel Glenn rode around the earth three times in Friendship 7. He took with him the emotions and prayers of millions who followed his flight almost minute by minute, especially during the suspenseful moments of reentry when his life was apparently in danger.

Even before the Glenn flight generated high national morale, it was apparent to many that Project Mercury, if successful, needed to be followed by a major challenge in space that would focus our national technological genius on a single dominating objective. Someone once said that the surest requirements for success were a definite objective and limited time. On May 25, 1961, President John F. Kennedy simultaneously defined that objective and gave it a needed timetable. The United States, the President said, should achieve the goal "before this decade is out, of landing a man on the moon and returning him safely to earth. No single space project in this period will be more impressive to mankind, or more important for the long-range exploration of space."

Sixteen months later, at Rice University in Houston, he supplied his answer to those who were already beginning to ask the question "Why the moon?"

"We choose to go to the moon in this decade," he said, "not because that will be easy, but because it will be hard — because that goal will serve to organize and measure the best of our energies and skills — because that challenge is one we are willing to accept, one we are unwilling to postpone, and one we intend to win."

With this presidential declaration of objectives, given long before many people had yet surmised the true and long-range significance of such a mission, the means by which man would reach the moon were boldly defined. In the process man could discover, even at the same time his planet became more polluted and despoiled, whether he did, indeed, have a significant destiny on heavenly bodies besides his mother earth.

# 5

# Why the Moon?

*What do we want of the vast worthless area? This region of deserts, of shifting sands and whirlwinds of dust? To what use could we ever hope to put these deserts or these endless mountain ranges? What use can we have for such a place? I will never vote one cent from the public treasury.*

> —SENATOR DANIEL WEBSTER, opposing mail service to the Far West and California more than 125 years ago, in a speech before Congress.

IF THE EARLY APOLLO ASTRONAUTS had chosen to land in the dark portion of the moon and had deliberately set off a large and powerful strobe light aimed at the earth, we would have been able to see the light about two seconds later. This means that the moon, long thought of as remote and unattainable, is less than two seconds away at the speed of light, which travels 186,000 miles per second.

Any speculation about where the moon came from and how it originated must take into account that two seconds of light travel is a very tiny increment in the vastness of the universe. At the speed of light, our nearest planet, Venus, is two minutes, fifteen seconds away at its

closest point. The sun is eight minutes, twenty seconds
away. The nearest star, Alpha Centauri, is 4.3 light-years
away, and the nearest galaxy, Andromeda, is 2.2 million
light-years away. Estimates of the distances from earth
to the recently discovered quasars range from 300,000 to
300,000,000 light-years away. In contemplating these
tremendous reaches of the universe, it is important to remember that the moon and earth are essentially a two-
planet "system," nearly joined, like a raft and a smaller
skiff drifting together in the mid-Pacific Ocean. Another
way of thinking about earth-moon travel is to realize that
at the earthly freeway speed of seventy miles per hour,
you could reach the moon in four and a half months. A
jetliner traveling only five hundred miles per hour could
reach it in three weeks.

The fact of the moon's closeness to us is comple-
mented by another elemental fact: the moon's relatively
large size in comparison to the size of the earth. Its diameter of 2,160 miles (compared to the earth's diameter of
7,927 miles) makes it nearly the size of North America
and South America combined, or about fifty-five times
the size of Texas. In size relationship to its planet, our
moon is far larger than any known moon anywhere else.
Little Deimos, one of Mars's moons, for instance, is only
about five miles in diameter, and Deimos's sister moon,
Phobos, is only ten miles in diameter. Jupiter has a dozen
moons, the largest of which is less than one ten-
thousandth of the huge mass of Jupiter. Of Saturn's ten
moons, only one is larger than our moon and it is
dwarfed by Saturn's large size (75,100 miles in diameter), as Jupiter's moons are by Jupiter's size. One of

Neptune's moons is about the same size as ours but since Neptune is 31,000 miles in diameter, it, too, is a dwarf moon in comparison with its planet. No other known planet has a satellite one-quarter of its own size and an average of only 238,856 miles away. If we think of the earth as a tennis ball, the moon is slightly larger than a Ping-Pong ball.

The third intriguing fact about the moon is how it rotates. The moon circles the earth counterclockwise once every 27.3 days, always keeping the same side — what we call the front side — toward earth. Traveling through space, the earth and moon move together around their common center of gravity, called the barycenter. It is important to remember that something had to put the moon at or near its present circular pattern around the earth. Just as an Apollo spacecraft circling the earth every ninety minutes while one hundred miles high has to have a velocity of roughly 18,000 miles per hour to stay in orbit, so something had to give the moon the precisely required velocity for its weight and altitude. For instance, it could not have been blown out from earth at some random speed or direction. We found this out when we first began to try to orbit artificial satellites. We discovered that unless the intended satellite reached a certain altitude at a certain speed and on a certain course parallel to the surface of the earth, it would not have the necessary centrifugal force to maintain the delicate balance with the gravity of earth which would permit it to remain in the desired orbit.

At old Cape Canaveral on the night of March 5, 1958, for instance, I watched the launch of Explorer 2 which was scheduled to be the second U.S. satellite to orbit successfully. Everything worked perfectly until the fourth and final stage attempted to achieve the required precise velocity, altitude and speed. On this occasion the difficult combination was not achieved and our intended satellite very soon plunged back into earth's atmosphere and consumed itself in the fire caused by its high-speed friction against our atmosphere.

To illustrate just how "chancy" it is to achieve a lasting orbit, it is worthwhile to look for a moment at the classic model of how the orbit of a satellite is achieved. It has sometimes been pointed out that if you could somehow put a cannon on a platform one hundred miles above the earth, you would be in a position to initiate an orbit because you would be high enough to avoid the drag of the atmosphere. Now, suppose we fire a cannonball on a course exactly parallel to the earth's surface at a speed of exactly 18,000 miles per hour. During the first second, as a result of the pull of the earth's gravity, the cannonball will fall sixteen feet. It will also travel a distance of five miles. The reason it will stay in orbit is that it so happens that the curvature of the earth drops sixteen feet every five miles. Inertia, or centrifugal force, can thus exactly counterbalance the pull of gravity.

The speed required for orbit changes every time either the altitude or the weight of the intended satellite is altered and objects farther away from the earth require more time to circle the earth. For the moon's distance and weight, that time, called the orbital period, is approximately 27.3 days. The point — and it is one seldom noted in considering the origin of the moon — is that it is extremely unlikely that any object would just stumble into the right combination of factors required to stay in orbit. "Something" had to put the moon at its altitude, on its course and at its speed. The question is: what was that something?

Discovering what that something was, given the moon's known distance from earth, its known huge relative size, and its known way of rotating, has occupied astronomers, scientists and, more recently, engineers in an attempt to solve one of the most fascinating riddles known to men on earth.

There is one other "known" — or partially "known" — with which speculators have worked down through the centuries. This known is the nature of the moon's surface, and our knowledge of it is based on what man could perceive with his naked eye, with telescopes, with cameras and other instruments and, now, with samples and other data taken from the surface itself. Before we look at the various and conflicting explanations and theories concerning the moon, we'd best first look at what its surface, so unlike that of familiar earth, has told us in years past.

Before the invention of the telescope what we knew of the moon's surface was based on what could be seen with the unaided eye. A Danish astronomer, Tycho Brahe, who lived at the time of Shakespeare, saw the moon and planets just as we see them on a clear night. He observed them continuously with the deft visual perception of a dedicated scholar. In the rocky southern uplands of the moon, Brahe studied a great bowl of light some sixty miles across. He was particularly intrigued with the mysterious rays that emanated from the crater at the center of the bowl. These rays seemed to stretch nearly a thousand miles across the lunar features. Today this prominent crater is known by the name Tycho.

In the year 1609, an Italian, Galileo Galilei, heard a rumor of a strange "optik tube" which could make faraway objects appear close at hand. Intrigued and inspired, he constructed such a device himself and turned it toward the moon and stars. His discoveries destroyed forever the long-held notion that the earth was the center of the universe. With his optical tube, Galileo saw the moon's rough, uneven surface.

"I have been led to the opinion and conviction that the surface of the moon is not smooth, uniform, precisely spherical as a great number of philosophers believe it to be, but is uneven, rough and full of cavities and prominences, being not unlike the face of the earth, relieved by chains of mountains and deep valleys," Galileo wrote. Within five years Galileo's conclusions had been translated into many of the world's languages.

By 1647, a telescope 130 feet long permitted the first generally accurate moon map to be made by Hevelius of Danzig. It was Hevelius who had the rare privilege of naming some 250 lunar formations, calling the flat areas maria, the Latin word for seas, and naming lunar mountains after such earth mountain ranges as the Alps and Apennines.

An Italian Jesuit priest, Giovanni Riccioli, constructed a lunar map a few years later in which he retained Hevelius's names but added many, many names of prominent earth scientists to lunar formations.

As telescopes improved throughout the eighteenth and nineteenth centuries, astronomers and selenographers catalogued some 33,000 lunar features and estimated the heights of over 3,000 mountains. In modern times, such powerful telescopic installations as the Lick Observatory, the Lowell Observatory, the Wilson Observatory and the 200-inch Hale reflector, the earth's largest telescope, near Mount Palomar, California, have greatly refined our knowledge of lunar surface features.

With these powerful telescopes we learned of large formations called "walled plains," such as Clavius, 146 miles across (the location of the lunar station in the movie *2001 — A Space Odyssey*), Hipparchus, Plato and, the largest of all, Bailly, 183 miles in diameter and containing peaks 14,000 feet high. Most craters are gently sloping and saucer-shaped; many have a central cone. Some, however, are extraordinarily deep. Newton, for instance, near the moon's South Pole, sinks 20,000 feet, and its floor has never felt the rays of the sun. The great "Monarch of the Moon" is Copernicus, 56 miles across with terraced walls that sink 12,000 feet below the lunar surface. The crater Aristarchus is so bright that the nineteenth-century English court astronomer Sir William Herschel thought it was an erupting volcano. In the mid-1960s, scientists all over the world were intrigued by two reports, one Russian, one American, that a mysterious red or reddish-orange glow briefly appeared at a spot on the moon's surface.

The height of lunar mountains was originally determined by using simple trigonometry and measuring the length of mountain shadows in relation to the sun's position. The tallest peaks on the moon in the Doerfel and Libnitz ranges near the South Pole tower upwards to around 30,000 feet, approximately the same height as Mount Everest. The tallest mountain in the lunar Apennines, Mount Huygens, rises to about 20,000 feet. The lunar Alps are less high, but they contain a mysterious gash called the Alpine Valley that is over a hundred miles long. Scattered about the moon are smaller, winding, river-like features called sinuous rills.

Some changes have occurred on the moon during the years it has been observed by man. In 1866, astronomer J. F. Julius Schmidt noted that the walls of the crater Linné had caved in, creating a white spot that can be seen today. In 1958, a Russian astronomer, N. A. Kozyrev, recorded the escape of a whitish cloud of gas or dust from a peak in the crater Alphonsus. The first man-made surface change was observed on September 13, 1959, when two European astronomers saw an expanding cloud of some twenty-five miles in diameter rise up from the place where Russia's Luna 2 impacted the surface.

As knowledge and data about these various surface features and characteristics spread, a number of tentative explanations were put forth as to how the moon came to be what and where it is. A number of authorities believed for many years that craters were caused by the impact of asteroids, those mysterious bands of sun-orbiting rocks located between Mars and Jupiter, and meteorites. Unlike the earth, the moon has no atmosphere to burn up all but the largest of inbound objects, and even the smallest object drawn in by lunar gravity reaches the surface.

One explanation of the wall plains such as Clavius and Plato is that asteroids pierced the crust of the young moon, exploded violently, and hewed out enormous craters, widely scattering rock fragments and debris and forming visible rays, like spokes from the hub of a wheel. Such a blast would have been visible from earth had men been living at that time.

This so-called impact theory has been countered by those who believe that the moon's interior is, or was, molten lava. As the lava seeped upward in fissures, gas collected and eventually ruptured the surface in the kind of violent explosion made familiar to us by volcanoes. This is sometimes called the bubble theory or volcanic theory of crater formation.

Both these theories, plus the knowledge that the moon wobbles slightly on its axis, is slowing down as it orbits, is slowly moving further away from earth, and has a density roughly similar to that of earth, have been taken into account in trying to explain how the moon and the solar system originated.

One of the earliest theories of the genesis of the moon was advanced by the son of the famous evolutionist Charles Darwin, Sir George Darwin. He believed the moon was once a part of the earth now covered by the Pacific Ocean. Eons ago, he theorized, when the earth was a semisolid mass, the rotating earth spun off a huge bulge of molten rock which became the moon.

A more popular, but by no means universally accepted, explanation is that the moon was formed some four and a half billion years ago out of the same spinning cloud of dust, gas and rocks that formed the sun and the planets, including earth.

A third theory holds that the moon was formed far distant from earth as a small planet and was later captured by the gravity of the earth.

I have never talked to Sir George Darwin, of course, about his theory that the moon was torn out of the Pacific basin, but I have talked to a number of distinguished men about the other two theories. Before Apollo, none was so sure of his particular theory that he was prepared to state it as a fact.

In April 1964 I drove to California to write an article on the life and work of Dr. Harold Urey, the renowned geochemist who won a Nobel Prize in 1934. I spent nearly a week at Urey's home in La Jolla, at his office at the University of California in San Diego, and at California Institute of Technology in Pasadena where he was appearing as guest lecturer. Although he was then seventy-two, the mind of my gray-haired subject was clear, sharp and concentrated on the scientific furor then going on regarding the origin of the moon.

He told me at that time: "I believe the moon was captured by the earth and was not originally a part of it. If our planned explorations show the surface to be similar to the material I have found in meteorites, I am right. But if it turns out that the maria are largely *basaltic* [lava flows], I am wrong. The entire scientific world is eagerly awaiting the positive evidence, for the moon will very likely unlock the whole secret of the origin of the solar system."

In 1968, before Apollo, I flew to Flagstaff, Arizona, to spend several days with Dr. Eugene Shoemaker for an article assigned by the *New York Times Magazine*. Dr. Shoemaker, as head of the Astrogeological Center and a distinguished lunar scholar, had probably studied the moon as closely as all but two or three other living men. His theory was that the moon was once as much as four hundred times as large as it is now, but that it collided with a huge comet, creating an explosion that reversed the direction of the moon's orbit. The moon was sent spiraling away from earth, and it moves slightly more distant from earth each year.

Prior to the Apollo flights, none of the theories was accepted by all scientists. The knowledge to answer one of man's most tantalizing riddles was simply not available. As we are to see later in this book, the knowledge gained from the first few Apollo flights and the treasure of lunar samples they returned to earth has inspired not only variations on old theories but also new concepts based on facts no one had heretofore dreamed of.

Before Apollo there were other reasons for sending man to the moon besides the all important scientific and philosophic question of how the moon, earth, and solar system originated. To probe better the secrets of the distant universe, we needed a new base for optical telescopes and radio telescopes. On earth, optical telescopes must first penetrate the distorting swirls of the earth's increasingly polluted atmosphere. On the moon, especially on its back side away from electronic interference from earth, a splendid base exists for the erection of outward-gazing instruments. Before Apollo, no one knew for sure

*Eugene M. Shoemaker*

what minerals, elements or new combinations we might find on the moon. Our ability to obtain, analyze, and explore possible new combinations of minerals or elements alone eventually may justify man's trip to the moon.

In addition to outward-gazing instruments trained on the universe, the moon, like artificial satellites, is also a solid base for earth-gazing instruments that can study the full range of earth resources from weather to crops to ocean currents.

Still another reason for going to the moon is to establish a base from which other explorations — both manned and unmanned — can be staged, supplied and observed. Who among us knows what fortunate role the moon may play in communications to Mars, for instance, or possibly to points far more distant.

Before Apollo, speculation on the moon's origin and expectation that the answer was very close reached new levels. Many, like Dr. Harold Urey, felt we were on the verge of highly significant new answers to ancient questions. And many, also like Urey, felt man's intellect, logic and imagination were still groping in the dark.

This latter fact was brought home to me one afternoon in 1964 when I attended a memorable lecture by Urey in a Caltech chemistry lab. I think what I wrote about him at the time for *Science Year* still adequately reflects the pre-Apollo scientific passion on the part of earthmen to discover whence the moon and the planets came.

Dr. Urey's first Caltech lecture on the origins of meteorites had been given in Caltech's splendid, but rather formal, Becklan Auditorium.

"Rooted to a rostrum and a microphone," I wrote then, "the great teacher in him never quite got across even though his facts and figures were masterfully composed. 'I did poorly today,' he explained later. 'I'm afraid it turned out to be just another formal lecture.'

"At his request, the second lecture, on the origin of the solar system, was shifted to a chemistry lecture room where no microphone was required. Here, Harold Urey's incredible mind projected brilliantly amid the force and sincerity of his teacher's calling. Beneath his mass of gray hair, his bespectacled face became a study in volatile concentration as he pursed his lips, frowned, jutted his bull-doggish jaw, and delivered spontaneous gestures of emphasis. Hunched over, he strode from one end of the long, black lab table to the other, alternately folding his arms across his chest and stabbing the air dramatically. His unaccented and sonorous voice had the commanding quality of the late Charles Laughton. Here was a man in his element, making electric contact with his audience as he probed the sun's origin in space and time.

"Completely compatible with the spirit of the scientific attitude he personifies, Urey was meticulously careful to give proper credit to the works and ideas of others. He remained almost reverently respectful of dissenting opinions thrown at him from individuals in his distinguished audience. Above all, he was transparently honest in his search for truth.

" 'Most of us agree on this model of the origin of the solar system,' he summarized. 'We came from a disc of dust and gas rotating in a plane about the sun. How did the planetary bodies and the asteroids form? They came from this disc of gases formed from the sun as it condensed. This is the best answer that any of us can hope for at the present. We are still seeking.'

"He laid down the long, wooden pointer he has learned to handle with the dexterity of a master swordsman, arranged his rough notes in a neat pile, and brushed off the omnipresent classroom chalk as students and professors alike surged around him seeking more answers to ponderous and difficult questions."

# 6

# Triumph and Disaster— the Tragedy on Pad 34

*Another of the consequences of the openness of NASA's manned space program is that sooner or later we may have an unpredictable, a very public, and very conspicuous failure. We must face up to the fact that somewhere in our exploration of our newest frontier we may have casualties . . . In complex mechanisms, including, of course, human beings, the possibility of failure does exist.*

— ASTRONAUT JOHN GLENN, 1964

*There's always a possibility that you can have a catastrophic failure. Of course, this can happen on any flight. It can happen on the last one as well as the first one. So, you just plan as best you can to take care of all these eventualities, and you get a well-trained crew and you go fly.*

— ASTRONAUT VIRGIL GRISSOM, 1966

AFTER PRESIDENT KENNEDY'S ANNOUNCEMENT in 1961 that an important American objective was to send men to the moon, the entire U.S. manned spacecraft program took on a new sense of urgency and destiny. I could feel the excitement each time I went to Cape Canaveral to see one of the manned launches of Project Mercury. Our space program, which now had both a specific objective and a timetable, was also tremendously stimulated by what the Russians were doing. Although both Russia and the United States denied they were in a race to the moon, many people automatically evaluated each of their manned flights as an indication of who had the best chance of being first on the moon.

At first the Russians seemed to be well out in front. After the Glenn shot, for instance, newspapers everywhere, especially in countries behind the Iron Curtain, pointed out a sort of box score: two orbital flights (Gagarin and Titov) for the Russians; one orbital flight (Glenn) for the United States.

At 7:45 on the morning of May 24, 1962, the country watched the liftoff of Aurora 7, as Scott Carpenter went successfully into the second orbital flight. Like John Glenn he orbited three times, then landed long — some 250 miles from the carrier *Intrepid*. But even with the off-course landing, his flight brought us that much closer to the moon.

"Isolated data points mean nothing," Scott commented after his flight. "Now through John Glenn's flight and my flight we have two data points on nearly everything that was observed. His flight confirms mine, and mine confirms his. And we have much more solid background now."

On the next Mercury mission, that of Sigma 7 on September 28, 1962, Wally Schirra's six-orbit flight proved that American astronauts could survive in space for nearly eight hours while a spacecraft orbited in drifting flight. But the Russians were staying ahead in the number of orbits achieved. In two previous flights, Pavel Popovich and Andrian Nikolayev had orbited the earth 48 and 64 times respectively. As 1963 dawned, however, the U.S. nearly doubled its time-in-orbit experience with the successful 22-orbit flight of Leroy "Gordo" Cooper.

After Cooper's flight, the last in the Project Mercury series, a long period of intense preparation began that was directly related to our moon mission. The one-man Mercury capsule had been designed merely to orbit the earth, checking out life support systems and rudimentary flight operations including communications and navigation. The program scheduled to follow it, Project Gemini, was directly designed to support our forthcoming flight to the moon. A long period of design and check-out time was required to develop the advanced equipment and techniques necessary to maneuver a spacecraft, to rendezvous and dock, and to remain in space for up to two weeks. As it turned out, the delay between Mercury and Gemini amounted to nearly two years.

While vital Gemini preparations were going on, the diversity and magnitude of the growing United States space program enabled the spacemen to try to use the time wisely. They concentrated on sending unmanned probes and automated spacecraft to the moon.

As early as August 23, 1961, I had seen our first attempt with the Ranger program fail as we tried to send a probe to the vicinity of the moon. Thereafter, both we and Russia continued to have a series of technical difficulties with automatic spacecraft bound for the moon. We learned much from our first six missions, even though their vital objective, sending back good close-up pictures of the moon, was delayed.

In July 1964, we finally achieved success with Ranger 7, which sent back the brilliant set of pictures I first showed to Neil Armstrong. The 4,308 initial Ranger pictures not only gave us our first close-up look at lunar craters that measured less than one yard in diameter, they also abolished, almost overnight, the theory that a thick dust layer might make it impossible for us to land on the moon and survive.

This knowledge was vital in the exact design of the footpads and landing gear of Project Apollo's lunar module. Fortunately Project Gemini was an intermediate step not requiring a lunar flight, and it progressed at the same time we gathered pictorial data on the nature of the lunar surface.

Gemini had been organized in late 1961 at a time when the nation and the world had been absorbed with man's first penetration of the cosmos. Its purposes were: to build a larger multicrewed spacecraft capable of long-duration flights and rendezvous and docking; to provide for practice in extravehicular activity (EVA), or astronaut experience outside the spacecraft, as a prerequisite to on-foot exploration of the lunar surface; and to practice the alternatives and perfect the techniques for safely entering the earth's atmosphere at various speeds and angles and effecting an accurate landing on earth.

During Gemini's long preparation many people continued to maintain that a race to the moon existed between the Soviet Union and the United States. While Gemini fell nearly a year behind its original schedule, space race exponents were pointing to evidence indicating the Russians might get to the moon first. In October

1964, Russia launched its three-man spacecraft Voskhod 1, which orbited sixteen times. Five months later, during the flight of Voskhod 2, with two men aboard, Colonel Aleksei A. Leonov became the first man to "walk" in space, thus anticipating one of Gemini's key objectives.

On March 23, 1965, the manned portion of the vital Gemini series began with the liftoff of a powerful Titan rocket carrying Virgil "Gus" Grissom and rooky astronaut John Young. Their brand-new and more commodious Gemini spacecraft weighed 8,360 pounds, 5,360 pounds more than the Mercury capsule.

The pioneer Gemini flight of three orbits was highly successful. In fact, Project Gemini had been prepared for so carefully that during its first year and a half, the United States averaged one flight every two months.

From Gemini 4 one of our most popular astronauts, Edward H. White, under the coaching of spacecraft commander James McDivitt, made the first American space walk. Ed enjoyed the excitement so much that he had to be ordered several times to reenter Gemini.

In Gemini 5, Gordo Cooper, sometimes called "Gordo the silent," and short, Princeton-graduate Charles "Pete" Conrad, who is anything but silent, checked out the new fuel cells as a source of power and palatable water in a 191-hour successful flight.

In late 1965, veteran Wally Schirra, the "textbook" pilot, and newcomer Thomas Stafford in Gemini 6 successfully rendezvoused with Frank Borman and Jim Lovell in Gemini 7. The two crews got as close as one foot from each other. They communicated by both radio and hand-written messages held against window ports.

Once, Annapolis graduate Wally Schirra held up a sign designed to kid West Point graduate Frank Borman. *Beat Army*, the sign read.

When Borman and Lovell returned from their two-week flight, the longest manned flight made by either Russia or the United States, examining physicians found them in apparent excellent health. From this point forward, there was little doubt in anyone's mind that man could safely survive a one-week flight to the moon and back.

In Gemini 8, launched March 16, 1966, command pilot Neil Armstrong and David Scott successfully rendezvoused with the unmanned Agena target vehicle, but later in this mission the misfire of a thruster caused severe bucking and wild spinning. The crew brought a highly dangerous situation under control, but Gemini 8 had to make an immediate emergency landing in the Pacific.

The final four Gemini flights repeated and refined rendezvous and docking techniques and EVA experience. In Gemini 9, Eugene Cernan and Tom Stafford practiced three alternative approaches to the Agena target vehicle. In Gemini 10, John Young and Michael Collins rendezvoused with two objects in space, first with their own Agena target, then with the Gemini 8 Agena which was still circling the earth. On September 12, 1966, Pete Conrad and Richard Gordon ignited their Agena's main engine to take a long, spectacular uphill ride 851 miles away from earth. Their return to earth could thus rehearse the return from the moon.

The final flight of the Gemini series, that of Gemini 12 with Jim Lovell and Edwin "Buzz" Aldrin, the first U.S.

space scientist, ended on a high note of optimism. With ten successful Gemini flights totaling nearly one thousand hours of successful manned space flight experience, the prevailing mood for the forthcoming check-out flights and lunar flights in Project Apollo was highly optimistic and affirmative.

At the press conference terminating the Gemini series, the director of Houston's Manned Spacecraft Center Dr. Robert R. Gilruth summed it up. "To go to the moon," he explained, "we had to learn how to operate in space. We had to learn how to rendezvous and dock, to light off large propulsion systems in space, to work outside the spacecraft, endure long-duration missions, and how to make precise landings from orbit. In the ten manned flights in eighteen months, we did all the things we had to do as the prelude to Apollo."

As I joined in the general celebrations in Houston, I talked to no one — neither officials nor astronauts — who did not seem to feel that Apollo would meet with the same success we had just seen in the Gemini program. None of us could then foresee that it was this same mood of confidence — or, perhaps, over-confidence — that was to contribute to the first tragedy in the United States space program.

If we can say that the difference between Project Mercury and Project Gemini is like the difference between a World War I Sopwith-Camel fighter plane and the World War II P–38 high-speed interceptor, then Project Apollo would represent the difference between a P–38 and an X–15 rocket plane. Just as the X–15 with its speed of 2,196 miles per hour represented a whole new concept of computer-aided aviation, so Apollo represented one tremendous and highly complex step forward, an ambitious step that was without precedent since the beginning of the industrial revolution. The project's involvement of 20,000 U.S. corporations, science departments of all major U.S. universities, ten NASA centers, over 300,000 people and, ultimately, over $25 billion, dwarfed even the digging of the Panama Canal and World War II's Manhattan Project which developed the first thermonuclear bomb.

Inherent in projects of such magnitude are tremendous risks. In aviation, revolutionary new hardware can be tested gradually in its intended environment by taxiing tests, by three-foot liftoffs from long runways and by initial short flights. In space, no such graduated exposure-correction process is possible. In effect, each one of over 300,000 parts must work perfectly on baptism in its intended environment. To compound the difficulty, Apollo had to carry the "state of the art" of rocketry a tremendous distance in a very short time. It was as if all the technological achievements which took place in the twenty-one years between our two world wars had to be compressed and telescoped into a half-dozen frenetically paced years. Without the time-saving factor and accuracy of modern computers, the task would have been quite impossible.

Those of us who had seen, heard, felt and smelled the explosions of one out of every three rockets we launched in the late Fifties could appreciate the task of building

APOLLO

X-15

U.S. AIR F

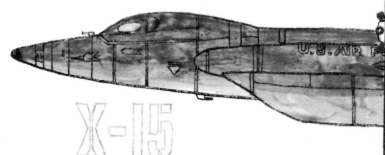

MERCUR

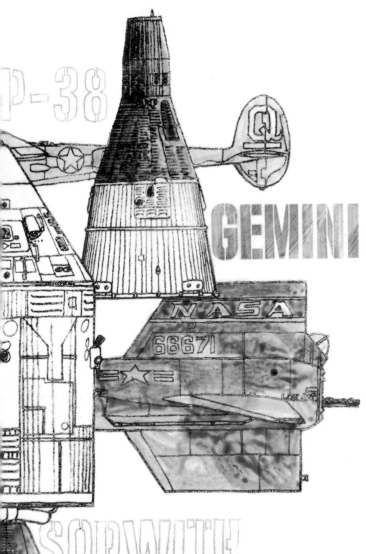

P-38

GEMINI

NASA

66671

SOPWITH
CAMEL

such reliability into the 281-foot-tall Saturn 5 rocket that all five of the booster engines in the first stage would simply ignite and fire correctly. But the reliability demands did not end with the main stage. We had to build not one spacecraft but two, the three-man command and service module (CSM) and the two-man lunar module (LEM). LEM had an overriding requirement that no manned spacecraft ever had before: to land on a solid object in a vacuum and to launch itself in the same vacuum after shutting down its propulsion system.

The plan finally accepted for going to the moon was felt by many engineers to be the simplest of three alternatives. The astronauts would first go into earth orbit, then fire up for the long translunar trajectory over approximately a quarter of a million miles of cislunar space. They would go next into a parking orbit of the moon, and then detach LEM for a direct descent to the surface. For the return, LEM would blast off for an immediate lunar orbit rendezvous with the command and service module. After crew transfer, LEM would be jettisoned, and the CSM would fire up for the transearth trajectory toward home. Finally, the CSM would make a direct entry into the earth's atmosphere, bypassing an earth orbit, and with the aid of parachutes effect a pinpoint landing.

After a series of unmanned check-out flights with the intermediate and small Saturn boosters, the first manned Apollo flight was scheduled for early 1967. No twenty-two-month gap such as the "downtime" between Mercury and Gemini was to be permitted. A bare three months after Lovell and Aldrin had splashdowned in

Gemini 12 on November 15, we now were able to go right into manned flight with a totally new system.

Selected as the prime crew for Apollo's maiden voyage in earth orbit was Virgil "Gus" Grissom, who was to be the first astronaut scheduled to fly in all three United States spacecraft; personable Ed White, who had made our first spacewalk in Gemini 4; and newcomer Roger Chaffee, a Navy officer and graduate of Purdue University. Gus, as commander, was to fly left seat, following the aviation tradition in which the first pilot, or captain, always sits on the left. The middle seat belonged to the next in astronaut rank, Ed White, and Roger Chaffee was assigned the right seat.

At midday on the warm blue-sky day of January 27, 1967, Grissom, White and Chaffee rode the elevators to the top of the 224-foot Saturn 1 rocket (called the up-rated Saturn 1) to rehearse for launch and to help check out the first Apollo spacecraft, number 012. Although no flight was scheduled, they were suited up since the hatch was to be closed while they tested, among other things, the life support system. Although a very realistic count-down was underway, there was no fuel in the Saturn rocket. Since the presence of fuel was regarded as the chief source of danger on a launch pad, no one regarded the rehearsal as a risky operation. For this reason, neither firemen nor doctors had been ordered to report to the pad.

At 1 P.M., Gus climbed in, crossed over two seat positions and took his command seat next to the left wall. Then White and Chaffee in turn took their positions, strapped themselves in and closed the three sections of the hatch. Slowly the cabin filled with pure oxygen and the pressure increased to scheduled launch pressure, 16.7 pounds per square inch.

Check-out work proceeded erratically through the long afternoon. There were a number of irritating delays, including an unexplained odor in the oxygen supply, and excessive static and faulty connections in the voice communications link. At one point Grissom voiced his frustration with the communications delays. "How do you expect to get us to the moon," he asked into his helmet mike, "if you people can't even hook us up with a ground station? . . . Get with it out there!"

Just after 6:30 P.M. a brief surge in the alternating current voltage gave an instrument reading which caused White's heart rate to jump up momentarily, but then everything settled back to normal. All readings on temperature, pressure and life support systems were nominal.

Then, suddenly — at three seconds after 6:31 P.M. — Apollo blockhouse personnel and a few people still on the pad heard the word "Fire!" through the communications static. Blockhouse instruments showed cabin pressure begin to rise. A jumble of confused words came through the intermittent static: "I've . . . we've," then, "We've got a fire in the cockpit . . . a bad fire . . . open her up . . . let's get . . . we're burning up . . ." Then there was a cry of pain. The cry, like the urgent words preceding it, could not positively be attributed to any one astronaut. Blockhouse instruments showed cabin pressure rising almost to the bursting point. Then the cabin did burst. Its tough aluminum hide ruptured in a long crack, and forced flame and smoke

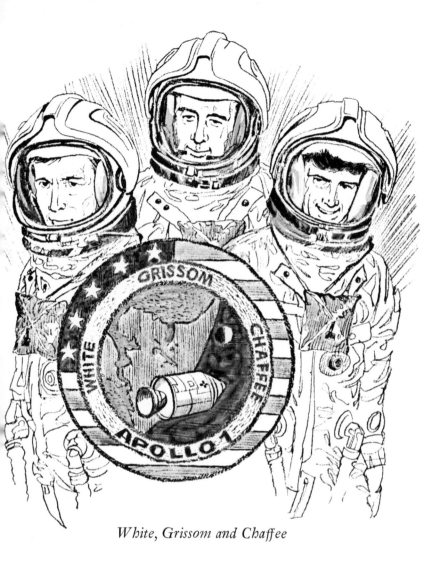

*White, Grissom and Chaffee*

down inside the rocket's ring of empty space. The explosion erupted at the rocket's base. The expelled concussion almost knocked the pad leader, Don Babbitt, off his feet. He collected himself and yelled for help. A number of the pad workers inside the gantry, thinking the entire rocket was exploding, raced for the elevators. But three of them, Steve Clemmons, Jim Gleaves and Jerry Hawkins, grabbed $CO_2$ fire extinguisher bottles and raced with Babbitt to the white room adjoining the hatch at the top of the rocket. There, in a room thick with dark smoke, they began to struggle with the hatch. Some had to fall back to find gas masks, but the masks, designed for poison gases rather than smoke, offered little protection. Inexplicably, no fire extinguisher was available in the white room. As they wrestled with the hot hatch, they worked with the very real fear that the overheated spacecraft would ignite the explosive torpedo of the escape rocket which was the only natural explosive in the entire rocket. It was located just above the spacecraft. The rocket was filled with solid fuel — essentially gunpowder — and its explosion could have killed them. They continued to fight at the outer hatch, the middle hatch and, finally, the inner pressure hatch.

When the final door opened, five full minutes had elapsed since the first report of fire. Heat and smoke poured out. The rescuers called inside. There was no answer. Eventually, Don Babbitt recognized cabin and instrument lights glowing dimly through the smoke. Then he saw a figure he presumed to be the immobilized figure of White in a blackened spacesuit with the helmet visor closed. White was on his back, arms outstretched toward the hatch. Another still form also showed an inert arm reaching for the hatch. Shaken, Babbitt retired to a phone and advised the ground that he would not comment at that time on what he had found inside. He was conscious of the fact that any comment he made would go through the entire communications net.

Three doctors reached the spacecraft nine minutes after fire was first reported. "It was evident," one of them said later, "that the crew had not survived the heat, smoke and thermal burns."

Because some of the space suit material had fused with the melted nylon surrounding the crewmen's contour couches, the bodies were not removed until two o'clock in the morning.

As news of the tragedy reached the astronauts' families and the world, it was apparent that three of our best astronauts had been killed on the verge of an adventure each of them had elected, and that they had died in a manner few had considered possible. It was also apparent that Project Apollo had been stopped dead in its tracks.

## 7

# Tragedy Overcome

*If we die, we want people to accept it. We are in a risky business, and we hope that if anything happens to us it will not delay the program. The conquest of space is worth the risk of life.*

— Astronaut Virgil Grissom

I HAD ATTENDED astronaut funerals before, but none was quite as sad as those which followed the tragedy on pad 34.* At previous funerals of individual astronauts killed in training aircraft it had been the practice for other astronauts to fly a "missing plane" formation above the flat Texas plains after the memorial church services in one of the small communities surrounding the Manned Spacecraft Center. As the jets roared overhead, a single missing plane in the formation symboled the missing astronaut. But now there were three missing astronauts, and around one of them, Ed White, there had collected that rare and charismatic blend of admiration and respect that — even

---

* Prior to the Apollo disaster, six U.S. astronauts had been killed: Ted Freeman, Charles Bassett, Elliot See, Clifton Williams, and Robert Lawrence, Jr., in aircraft accidents and Edward Givens in an automobile accident. Lawrence was a Negro astronaut assigned to the Air Force's Manned Orbital Laboratory Project, which was later canceled.

in the unemotional climate of the Texas space center —
could only be described as incipient hero worship. How
could a plane formation flying over the burial services at
Arlington National Cemetery in Washington symbolize
a triple loss of such magnitude? To compound the sadness and grimness of the occasion, NASA's attempt to
withhold the tape recording of the astronaut's last des-
perate words and cries had been frustrated by the press
on the very day of the funeral. Scarcely a person who attended the memorial services at Arlington had not read of
those last, pain-wracked words in the morning paper.

The impact of those words on the family seemed
harsher even than the gloom of the funeral itself,
especially on the face of Mrs. Edward White, a fragile
woman whose delicate features reflected the same grief-
struck beauty and dignity that characterized the faces of
Mrs. John F. Kennedy and Mrs. Martin Luther King in
their own moments of trial.

The mood of the funeral was that these men, like Kennedy and King, had been sacrificed because they were
fulfilling self-elected roles of leadership.

Even the blasé façade of my fellow journalists was
affected. A friend of mine, George Alexander, the
"pool" reporter representing all of us, was the first permitted to look inside the spacecraft after the bodies had
been removed. When I talked to him after he inspected
the fatal spacecraft, he seemed — despite long experience
in observation and perception — quite incapable of de-
scribing the charred straps, fused nylon, melted solder
and ruptured aluminum oxygen lines that had met his vision.

As in all major tragedies, the full implication took awhile to sink in. The first and overriding question was: would less haste on the part of NASA to meet the strenuous Apollo deadlines have avoided the accident? As time passed, this question drew an increasingly affirmative answer.

President Johnson ordered a full investigation. Eventually over a thousand technical experts were consulted. In subsequent reports of both NASA's board of inquiry (which contained some astronauts) and congressional subcommittees, serious errors and oversights were uncovered and ruefully admitted. The Apollo spacecraft contained nothing with which to extinguish a fire but a toy water pistol used for drinking. To place and turn a ratchet on the inner pressure door and then to open the other two hatch layers from the inside required ninety long seconds. No automatic release mechanism for the hatch had been provided.* In certain places, unprotected electrical wiring was subject to chafing by other cockpit equipment. In addition, plastic used in several places in the cockpit was highly inflammable. Electrical joints were widely sealed with solder, which melts easily, inviting sparks. Aluminum oxygen line joints were also subject to melting, thus allowing the escape of more fire-feeding oxygen. Certain liquids used for cooling purposes were also unnecessarily combustible. The fatal

---

* This NASA decision was based partly on the fact that on Grissom's first Mercury flight in Liberty Bell 7, his automatic hatch release mechanism had accidentally gone off while he was floating on the water. The accident, which nearly caused Grissom to drown, resulted in the sinking of his spacecraft.

spacecraft, 012, had not been given any adequate vibration test. To compound these derelictions, an earlier and critical report, called the Phillips Report, which had pointed out some of these and other deficiencies, had been suppressed from the public and Congress alike by NASA. Had the report been made public, some safety corrections most certainly would have been demanded prior to the first flight. The need for these corrections could have been realized by anyone who has ever seen a glowing ember at the end of a stick turn into a white-hot fire when the stick is placed inside an oxygen flask in a chemical lab. Simple logic would deduce that 100 percent oxygen under pressure in a cabin stuffed with electrical paraphernalia was a potential lethal environment for man.

Although the exact cause of the fire was never pinpointed, it was believed to have been started by an electrical spark that emanated from the left or command pilot's side of the spacecraft. The initial fire ignited nylon and other cockpit inflammables, melted connections and expanded as more oxygen fed it. Then as the spacecraft ruptured under twenty-nine pounds per square inch of pressure, the fire was spread by the vortex created by the outward-rushing air.

The three-thousand-page report of the official investigation was a long catalogue of what it referred to as "deficiencies in design and engineering, manufacturing and quality control."

The official cause of death was listed as "asphyxiation by carbon monoxide." Surprisingly, the heavily layered astronaut's pressure suits had afforded more protection from "thermal burns" than anyone had thought possible. There were some burns but they were not severe enough to have been listed as the major cause of death.

Following the disaster, Apollo entered a period of new tests and major new modifications to make the cockpit safe for the now admittedly dangerous pressurized oxygen environment. During this long period, I watched thousands and thousands of feet of film as it came into NASA from contractors and subcontractors that showed progress in both a series of intricate flammability tests and also in alternate methods of handling cockpit wiring and plumbing. When I visited NASA laboratories and workshops, coffee breaks were brief and puns and jokes were few. What was new about the prevailing serious mood was that it was caused not by the former anxiety about meeting a time schedule, but by the more human concern that no more astronauts would be lost due to poor quality control or human error.

About two months after the Apollo tragedy of January 1967, when estimates on the length of the delay were becoming increasingly pessimistic, speculation was revived that the Russians now had a chance to overtake us in the race to the moon. The Russians had not launched a man flight since the March 18, 1965 Voskhod flight during which Colonel Leonov had taken the first walk in space. Rumors were rampant in Russia that the Soviets were on the verge of launching their own third-generation spacecraft, the equivalent of Apollo. Those who believed the Russians were still in a race to the moon were certain that one of the first tasks of the new vehicle would have to be rendezvous and docking. Their belief centered on the fact that rendezvous and docking was essential both to lunar flights and to the assembly of space stations in orbit. And while we had completed ten rendezvous experiments in Gemini and had docked nine times, manned Soviet spacecraft had never gotten any closer in orbit than about three miles.

On April 23, 1967, the rumors were confirmed by a Tass announcement that a new spacecraft called Soyus (pronounced Suh-yōōsh, meaning "Union") had been launched with a single pilot aboard. The name of the pilot was Cosmonaut Colonel Vladimir Komarov. Komarov was one of the Russian space pilots I had talked with when I went to the Soviet Union in 1966 to gather material for a book on the Soviet space program.* He and I had talked at length through an interpreter. Neither of us knew then, of course, that he was to be the next cosmonaut in space. I found him a handsome, polite and friendly man. His relaxed personality was not unlike that of many of my astronaut friends in Texas. Komarov, whose favorite American astronauts were John Glenn and Scott Carpenter, talked about the Soviet space program in general and related several amusing stories about life in the "cosmonaut village" just outside Moscow. At the conclusion of our interview, he smilingly presented me with a gold and ruby pin from his military tunic, and I gave him my Gemini tie clasp. I liked him.

It was with a sense of personal sadness that I heard through Tass that the initial Soyus flight, like our first

---

* *Soviet Space Exploration: The First Decade*. New York: Washington Square Press, 1968.

Apollo attempt, had ended in tragedy. Komarov had been killed, Tass reported, when he tried to reenter the earth's atmosphere on his eighteenth orbit. Although the cause of the Soyus disaster was widely debated in the U.S. press, I had occasion later, following the investigation of an official Soviet board of inquiry, to question separately three knowledgeable Russians about it: academician Leonid Sedov, one of the leading Soviet space scientists, cosmonaut-scientist Konstantin Feoktistov and cosmonaut-general Georgi Beregovoy.

Each told me in his own way the cause of the accident. Soyus, they said, used one main parachute and a smaller auxiliary parachute. The main parachute, they said, became fouled by the auxiliary parachute just after attempted deployment. Soyus hit the ground at nearly full speed and Komarov was killed instantly. The interpreter who translated Beregovoy's explanation to me omitted one part of the general's reply. When the difficulty occurred, the cosmonaut said, it was too late for Komarov to use his personal parachute.

The fact that the first known manned Soviet space setback followed our own by less than three months was an astonishing coincidence. In an article I wrote for *Fortune* magazine later that year, I pointed out nine other similar coincidences between major events in the space programs of the two rival nations. In fact, in terms of history, every major technical achievement of the first decade of space exploration of both programs, except for rendezvous and docking, took place in the same time span — roughly within three months of one another. While the coincidences in achievement could be explained by factors other than chance, it was now clear that the first major setback in manned spacecraft design was *entirely* coincidental. And the Soyus failure was a major setback. Academician Sedov told me, "A large amount of modification work was done."

Thus, throughout the downtime of the remainder of 1967 and of early 1968, the U.S. and the U.S.S.R. were equally busy in correcting the faults of Apollo and Soyus. As it turned out, the delay caused to both sides was — also coincidentally — about the same number of months.

I spent part of this time getting acquainted with two of our astronauts, Walter Cunningham and Donn Eisele, who were now scheduled to join veteran Wally Schirra in Apollo 7, the first flight scheduled after the fire. Since I had an assignment to write and produce a biographical film for television on each of the Apollo 7 crewmen, I spent much time reviewing thousands of feet of NASA film taken during astronaut training and Wally Schirra's two previous flights. Occasionally I talked to Cunningham and Eisele in the office they shared on the third floor of the ultramodern astronaut office building not far from the main MSC cafeteria.

Donn Eisele, a 150-pound Air Force major and Naval Academy graduate, was much the shyer of the two. He had a quick but shy smile, reminiscent of that of astronaut John Young, the first second-generation astronaut to get a flight. When I mentioned to Eisele that I had had a lot of trouble finding film footage of him taken during astronaut geology and survival-training field trips, he smiled and said, "I know the reason for that. Every time I saw the cameraman coming my way, I'd move off until I was behind him, where he'd already taken pictures." But Eisele, who since becoming an astronaut had attended the funerals of his father, mother and son Matthew, was his own man. When he needed to make a point he believed in, he was quite capable of making it with conviction and force.

Walt Cunningham, a former Marine major now a civilian, was not the sort of man you'd like to compete with in hand-wrestling, Indian wrestling, handball, or anything else. He had an average frame but he had the rugged windblown features of an outdoorsman and was broad-shouldered and rock-hard from his constant gym work, especially on the handball court and trampoline. Once he had bounced so hard on the trampoline that he came down off-target and off-balance and fractured a vertebra in his neck. "But don't put that in the film," he said with a laugh. "People will say they're sending a guy with a broken neck into space."

Wally Schirra, of course, had enough fame and status from his previous flights to make things rough on any NASA bureaucrat or aerospace contractor who didn't do things the way he wanted them done. Like Alan Shepard, the most affected and therefore the least popular of the original seven astronauts, Schirra had a touch of "celebrititus," but, unlike Alan Shepard, he kept it within reasonable bounds and used it as some women use their beauty and charm, only when it really mattered. What really mattered to Schirra was that no goofs, or what he called quaintly "a funny kind of thing," were going to spoil their chances with the newly modified

Apollo spacecraft. He was quite aware that the tragedy that had taken Grissom, White and Chaffee underscored every objection he chose to make, and at countless design review and project status meetings, he chose to make a lot of objections. He usually got what he wanted. He had also announced that at forty-five years of age he had decided to make this his last flight. This, perhaps, added to his boldness.

By the time of the last major spacecraft check-out on September 27, 1968, an estimated $75 million had been spent in Apollo modifications. A lion's share of the cost had gone into the development of a simpler, safer and quick-opening hatch. Schirra, Cunningham and Eisele expressed a high measure of confidence in their new vehicle when it passed all its late-September checks. Of the new seven-second hatch, Schirra said, "Other than putting ejection seats in, I see no faster way of getting out . . . We're ready for a hundred and sixty-four revolutions of the earth without a tire change."

The purpose of the initial earth-orbital flight of Apollo was to check out the command module's propulsion system and rendezvous maneuvers. No LEM was attached. The flight would be considered a success after three days, and it could last ten days. The main stage was not to be the monstrous Saturn 5 moon rocket, but the smaller Saturn 1B which stood twenty-two stories high.

The countdown for Apollo's premiere flight began October 6. Two days later doctors cleared all three crewmen for flight.

At 10:02 on the morning of October 11, 1968, the first flight of the ambitious project named for the Greek god of light and twin of Artemis, goddess of the moon, blasted up from the imposing-looking new facilities at the Kennedy Space Center. Cheers erupted as bright orange flame thrust the rocket slowly upward. It had been twenty-three months to the day since the last manned American space flight. America was back in space. Schirra's pulse rate at liftoff was a mild eighty-seven beats per minute. There was undoubtedly some truth to the belief, first expressed by the Russians, that a space pilot feels more secure in a "crowd" of three men.

After about seven hours of flight, the astronauts took off their gloves and helmets and looked around their commodious spacecraft. As a welcome change from earlier vehicles, there was room to stand up, float around and take "swimming exercises." Schirra had insisted on bringing coffee along and drank the first cup of coffee ever consumed in space.

The crew performed one of the vital parts of the mission when they pulled slowly away from the adapter and final rocket stage and, in rehearsal for the moon mission, turned the spacecraft around. They then approached within five feet of their detached hardware. They next let themselves drift farther away to get ready for the rendezvous practice the following day.

The next day Schirra reported the first U.S. space illness, a severe cold. Several people remembered that both Cunningham and Eisele had had colds just prior to the flight and that Schirra had gone dove hunting two days before liftoff. Partly because of his cold, spacecraft commander Schirra announced that he was canceling the first of a scheduled TV series from space in order to concentrate on the vital rendezvous maneuver. When "Deke" Slayton from Misson Control urged him to go on with the show, Schirra replied testily, "We have a new vehicle up here and I'm telling you at this point that TV will be delayed without any further discussion. . . . We do not have the equipment out. We have not eaten at this point. I have a cold. I refuse to foul up our time line at this point."

There was no TV show. The rendezvous maneuver from about a hundred miles out and dual firing of the propulsion system worked as planned. The maneuver was generally similar to the planned lunar rendezvous maneuver between LEM and the command module.

The next day Cunningham reported a stuffed-up nose and joined his commander in taking aspirin and decongestant tablets. This highly publicized method of treating the common cold, as prescribed from the ground by astronaut physician Dr. Charles Berry, started a flurry of newspaper advertisements in extremely poor taste by some overeager and intensely competitive manufacturers of aspirin and decongestant tablets.

On the third day of the Apollo 7 flight, members of the press assembled to watch the first live American TV show from space. The clear but slightly jerky pictures revealed a cheerful and playful crew despite the persistence of sniffles. Mimicking one of comedian Dean Martin's television lines, a grinning Schirra held up a sign reading, *Keep those cards and letters coming in, folks!* After some more horseplay, the crew, dressed in white coveralls, changed TV lenses and pointed the camera toward the Gulf of Mexico. Clouds and the Florida coastline were clearly visible approximately 150 miles below. The TV "show" concluded after seven minutes.

As the mission progressed, several difficulties developed that threatened, for a time, to shorten the flight. The number one electrical circuit failed briefly three times, apparently because of an overvoltage whenever one of two glycol fans was turned off. Another circuit also failed, but was quickly reactivated when the astronauts reset the circuit breaker. Had both circuits failed permanently, the flight would have had to have been recalled.

A second TV show confirmed that all three crewmen were still bothered by colds and sniffles. Schirra's mood continued to alternate between crankiness and "prankiness." Once, he chewed out the ground for waking him early, then mollified his ground controllers by holding up a sign reading, *Are you a TURTLE?* Since the required answer — in lieu of buying drinks — involved the use of a basic three-letter word sometimes used to describe a small donkey, Schirra successfully put down the men in Mission Control. The Interstellar Association of Turtles, Outershell Division, is a fun-loving association of astronauts and journalists. Members who are bold enough to respond with the correct answer are entitled to wear a small "turtle" lapel pin.

The middle phase of the vital check-out flight involved the sending of Morse code from space. The code is a backup means of communication that might be required if the primary wire channel failed. Simulation of lunar base communications, the repair of spacecraft plumbing, the check-out of guidance and navigation, and the tracking of Hurricane Gladys were also accomplished.

In three more TV "laugh-ins," which came to be known as the *Wally, Walt and Donn Show,* the crew demonstrated how space food is prepared in plastic bags. Schirra didn't mention on the TV show some difficulty he was having with a new high-calorie food mixture. He believed it was causing part, at least, of the crew's diarrhea problem. Privately he told the ground, "This high calorie stuff that's got everything all hiked up with calories is just really doing something to us. . . . It's all got a sweet taste. You think something tastes real good, but by the time you get to the end of the bag, you can't really look it in the eye very well."

Donn Eisele joined in by telling the control center that "Wally and I were trying to give away our butterscotch pudding, but no one wants it."

On their 105th revolution, they turned on the big, 21,000-pound thrust engine for sixty-six seconds. This was a significant test of the engine's space-start capability and efficiency. It worked beautifully; its powerful thrust briefly created a gravity similar to that on earth. The burn boosted the high point of their egg-shaped path around the earth from 177 miles to 280 miles.

Splashdown for Apollo 7 came in rough seas near Bermuda on October 22. In 163 orbits of the earth, covering over four million miles, no serious flaw in Apollo had developed.

A week and a half after splashdown, my wife Toby and I flew to the LBJ Ranch, about two hundred miles from Houston, to watch the crew show the remarkable flight film to President and Mrs. Johnson. We met in what was formerly the ranch airplane hangar. Now, as a press briefing room, it had been outfitted with a gold carpet, Pullman-colored drapes, acoustical ceiling and padded folding chairs. The President, holding a tan Stetson hat and wearing a fawn-colored suit and brown cowboy boots, watched attentively as Schirra explained the pictures taken of the earth, including some of Hurricane Gladys.

Afterwards, when someone asked Schirra if he had become angry in space, he meekly replied, "Our colds kept our heads full. We were very busy. Ten and eight-tenths days is a long time. I apologize to everyone for some of my remarks, as they were made offhand, but not for any of my decisions."

After the astronauts received NASA's Exceptional Service Medals (Schirra for the third time), Mrs. Johnson served coffee, soft drinks and cookies on the concrete ramp just outside the hangar. She, von Braun and I discussed the growing speculation that the next flight, Apollo 8, would have its mission changed so it could attempt to orbit the moon. "We are ready, Mrs. Johnson," he said in that resonant, German-accented voice that has uttered so many key directions in the space program. Even as we talked, a team in Mission Control was already rehearsing the circumlunar flight. Nine days later, in Washington, the decision was made to try to send Apollo 8 to the moon.

## 8

# Ten Times Around
# the Moon

*The overwhelming wonderment is why in the world we
can't appreciate what we have.*

— ASTRONAUT FRANK BORMAN

IN THE SUSPENSEFUL YEARS building up to man's flight to
the moon, hundreds of articles in newspapers and magazines and dozens of television programs tried to describe
what the grand adventure would be like. Without exception all those references looked forward not to the day
when man first circled and flew behind the moon, but to
the historic day he first stepped out on the untrodden
surface.

We now know how momentous that first step could
be. What we did not know prior to seeing that compellingly different Christmas moon of 1968 was how enthral-
ling man's first circumlunar flight would be. For the first
time man crossed the mysterious quarter-million miles of
void known as cislunar space, for the first time human
eyes saw the beckoning moon grow ever nearer, for the
first time man slowly circled above the moon's pristine
and timeless front side and its awesome back side on

which human eyes had never before rested. Man himself now could marvel close at hand at the moon's airless and deserted plains, its forbidding crater-pocked surface replete with towering, snowless mountains, deeply sloping waterless valleys and all the other wonders of a silent and unexplored island in space, a globed island without any beaches at all save for the black void of the firmament.

Apollo 8 was a "sleeper" flight. Its portent and astonishing implications crept up unexpectedly on the consciousness of man and captured his sense of wonder. The only ones prepared for the importance of the flight were the crew members, and even they, absorbed as they were in the minutiae of training and rehearsal and the mundane world of engineers who would forever walk on the surface of the earth, were not fully prepared.

One of the last things Jim Lovell did before he left for Cape Kennedy was put a Christmas package for his wife under the family tree of their comfortable home on Lazywood Lane. The package, which was not to be opened until Christmas, contained a new mink coat and a card which read, "from the man on the moon." Jim had meant it whimsically, yet the card gave a clue to his private appreciation of the magnitude of the voyage he was about to undertake.

There is little time for philosophy in the space business. Philosophy suggests individuality and, in the computer-oriented world of aerospace, men as well as machines are sometimes judged by their ability to interchange for one another. Yet philosophy came inevitably to each of those three men who participated in that journey.

Two of those selected to make the first flight to the moon were the most experienced astronauts in the world, Frank Borman and Jim Lovell, who flew separately in Gemini flights and had flown together for two weeks in Gemini 7.

Unlike Gordon Cooper and Pete Conrad, whose personal tensions preceding their Gemini 5 flight once erupted into a brief fistfight, Borman and Lovell got along splendidly. If personal friction could have occurred, it certainly would have during what Lovell had once called "two weeks together in a garbage can," the 5.7 million miles and 206 earth revolutions of the record-setting flight on Gemini 7. On that merciless endurance test, two grimy, beard-fuzzed men had worked, eaten and slept side by side for 335 hours without interruption, hearing and smelling each other like two male bears caged in a traveling circus.

For Frank Borman, who had graduated eighth in his West Point class of 670, the moon flight was to be his last voyage in space. It was to capstone a career that had often seemed an impossible dream. As a child in Gary, Indiana, he suffered from sinus trouble and had recurrent trouble with his tonsils, adenoids and ears. By the age of five, he had had two major operations including a mastoid operation. Partly to make things easier on the frail, slight youngster, his parents moved to the clear, dry desert air of Phoenix, Arizona. There his previously indifferent grades improved along with his health, enough to assure his acceptance to and graduation from West Point. Later he earned a master's degree in aeronautical engineering from Caltech. Electing a career in the Air

Force, he once was grounded after rupturing an eardrum while flying an F–80 jet. On another occasion, while flying at 36,000 feet at 1,500 miles per hour, the engine on his F–104 blew out and he chose to glide and land dead stick rather than bail out. When an application for the astronaut program became open to him, neither he nor Susan Borman, his pretty blonde wife from Tucson, hesitated. In Houston, he was quickly marked as an astronaut who had the rare ability to combine personal drive and ambition with consideration for other people. He thought for himself, yet was an ideal team man.

The middle-seat man, Jim Lovell, got his assignment by accident. When the formerly scheduled middle seater, Mike Collins, had to drop out for major surgery on his neck, Lovell moved up from the backup crew. He was a welcome addition; he had more hours in space than any other man on earth. He wore the sudden and unaccustomed mantle of fame as unaffectedly as an earlier astronaut, John Glenn, had worn it. He talked rather loudly, was nearly as full of raw energy and exuberance as Pete Conrad, and was never known to show discouragement. It was not for nothing that he was called "Smiling Jim." Other astronauts also occasionally called him "Shaky," not because he was nervous but because he was apt with a pun or quip and liked to "shake" people with unexpected laughs. His even, firm features made him good-looking without being pretty in the old Hollywood sense. He was what reporter Jim Maloney called a "poster-type astronaut." He liked sports cars and boats. He drove a series of Corvettes and sometimes liked to roar down Taylor Lake wide open in my 100-

horsepower outboard. His selection as chairman of the President's Committee on Physical Fitness was a natural one. He took time out from his rigid training requirements to make an effective film on America's need for better physical fitness. Because he recommended in the film that people bound to a desk should walk up stairs rather than take the elevator, all but a few astronauts started to use the stairs in three-story Building 4 instead of riding the elevator to their offices. Lovell ribbed those who didn't, and they liked it. Even his loyal wife Marilyn, who didn't really need to, took off a little weight.

The right-seat man was new to space, but he was not the sort of man anyone would call a rookie to his face. Thirty-five years old, Bill Anders was a crew-cut aeronautical engineer and former fighter pilot who held the Air Force rank of major. Born in Hong Kong as the son of a Navy commander this five-foot-eight, 145-pound man had the right combination of candor and professional approach to his responsibilities to fly with the world's most experienced spacemen.

Before his flight, when asked if his family was nervous, he replied, "Sure they are. So am I. I'd be a liar if I didn't say so. And we'll be the same way on the second flight."

On his thirtieth birthday, October 17, 1963, he had been accepted in the third class of U.S. astronauts (both Borman and Lovell were in the second class) and he was soon regarded as an intelligent, hard-working trainee. He had met Valerie, his slender wife from Lemon Grove, California, as opposite partners on a double date, and they and their five children lived in a comparatively modest house in the El Lago space center community.

Before leaving their homes in early December for the Florida space port, all three crew members celebrated an early Christmas with their children. The Lovells' Santa Claus gave James, thirteen, a pogo stick; Susan, ten, a pair of stilts; and two-and-a-half-year-old Jeffrey, whose birth had taken place just a few days after his father returned from space on his first Gemini flight, a small helicopter. Before he left, Frank Borman had a last romp with his kids and assured them that a special voice channel from Mission Control would be piped into their home so they could hear the "real time" dialogue which in some cases could be heard before the audio came over their color TV set. One of the last things Bill Anders said to his son Gregory, age six, was, "I'll deliver a message to Santa Claus for you."

The three voyagers got into their jets on December ninth and for the last time flew over their own tiny portion of the earth's surface. That portion was soon to merge into an unprecedented panorama as their own planet receded into the distance. The world then was seen entirely from pole to pole, and their particular part merged into a strangely moving and beautiful blue and white agate floating in time and space.

At the Cape they ran on the beach beside one of the earth's great oceans to get their bodies ready. Then they locked themselves inside austere mechanical mock-ups, practicing and rehearsing mind and reflex. Seldom — if at all — did they privately dream of the adventure that lay ahead.

On the night of December 20, 1968, the astronauts ate a steak dinner and went to bed. They were the only ones to sleep that night near that magic place where bluish arc lights focused on the world's mightiest rocket, the monstrous 36-story Saturn 5 being readied for its first live flight. Because of its previous check-out flights with ballast aboard, Saturn 5, the ultimate creation of Wernher von Braun and his group of former Peenemünde Germans, was now called "man-rated." But the three crewmen — above all Frank Borman, who had been on the Apollo fire accident investigating board — knew inviolately that no rocket is ever "man-rated" until man has safely flown in it. They slept near to the rocket's shadow while earth walkers and computers checked and rechecked the intended astro vehicle throughout the long night.

When the men were awakened in darkness, they didn't think of the target moon but of the weather, the local clouds and a hundred other things that could thwart and abort the day of beginning. Their human memory cells, so heavily laden, had been programed to think and respond in stages and this stage, essentially unrehearsed, was the "what if" stage. Each man thought of his own "what if's" and secretly applauded every passing minute that no negative "what if's" happened. They didn't dare believe it.

They got to the rocket; they went up the elevators; they got through the hatch, the harnessing up, the checklist. There were no delays.

On the morning of December 21, the final descending cadence of the countdown, spaced shorter than a heart pulse — especially the pulse of Frank Borman, which was now well over one hundred beats a minute and climbing fast — was tolled off. As the Russian prophet Konstantin Tsiolkovsky had said it thirty-seven years before:

Ten . . . *The earth* . . . nine . . . *is* . . . eight . . . *the cradle* . . . seven . . . *of humanity* . . . six . . . *but mankind* . . . five . . . *was not meant* . . . four . . . *to stay* . . . three . . . *in the cradle* . . . two . . . *forever* . . . one . . . We have commit . . . We have liftoff . . . Liftoff at 7:51 A.M. eastern standard time . . . We have cleared the tower . . . thirteen seconds.

As the great rocket rose on five erupting pulses of white-hot flame, an aerospace contractor named Paul White standing at a road block felt powerful reverberations rhythmically surge against his chest. He said to himself, "I've felt the earth tremble before, but now it's trembling me." Across the Cape, sitting inside the firing room, Terry Oyster, a bearded console monitor, felt his chair begin to quake. Turning, he watched the huge Plexiglass window behind him surge in and out as if it were made of cellophane.

Apollo 8 roared aloft, majestic and inexorable. Eleven minutes and 30 seconds later, velocity had reached 25,577 feet per second in a solid earth orbit. At 1 hour and 18 minutes into the flight, the crew felt a hundred beginning-of-the-day "what if's" slip into the past when five magic words cleared the way for man's longest journey: "You are go for TLI [translunar injection]."

"Roger," responded Frank Borman. "We are go for TLI."

*Apollo 8 liftoff*

"Nothing romantic," said NBC's David Brinkley, "nothing poetic, no philosophy; it's just, you are go for TLI."

"Go for TLI" became a fact 107 minutes later when the Saturn 4B booster ignited in one powerfully flaming burn that literally severed the tough sinews of earth's gravity. On board and in Mission Control, the men of Apollo 8 watched the readouts — the velocity buildup in feet per second — as the numbers snowballed.

"Okay, we've got SECO," Borman said, referring to the on-time engine cut off.

Shortly after cutoff occurred, the astronauts were traveling faster and higher than man had ever before gone. Apollo 8 now jettisoned hardware that had served its purpose. Still attached were the Saturn S–4B final-stage booster and a marvelous thinking and acting apparatus, the 4,400-pound ring of computerized equipment known as the instrument unit. "As the IU goes," von Braun had said before the flight, "so goes Saturn." IU, which had successfully guided the three earthlings into their coasting flight toward the moon, then too was discarded, marooned and monumented perhaps forever in endless orbits of the sun. Of the original Saturn rocket train, only the Apollo spaceship and its still-attached service module remained. The service module functioned very much like a portable filling station, supplying electric power, air and other expendables to the three men inside Apollo 8.

The crew turned around for a look back at earth. "Give us a clue as to what it looks like from way out there," asked the ground.

"Well Roger," said Jim Lovell. "I can see the entire earth now out the center window. I can see Florida, Cuba, Central America, the whole northern half of South America, in fact, all the way down through Argentina . . . and down through Chile."

"They picked a good day for it," the ground said.

Now Borman, Lovell and Anders settled down to the routine of the outward flight: systems checks, observations, navigational star sightings.

The accuracy of the navigator, Jim Lovell, would eventually earn him the epithet "the man with the golden fingers." The ground, amazed at his proficiency at his navigational chores, said to him at one point, "Jim, I've just been looking at your work with respect to accuracy and we figure you're within a couple of thousandths of a degree of the theoretical optimum"—a long way of saying he was right on the money. Lovell's accurate readouts were so swift that, at another point, the ground asked him to slow down so recording machines on earth could keep up with him. His performance set early accuracy standards that were to be characteristic of the entire mission.

On Sunday morning, December 22, before the Dallas vs. Cleveland football game came on television, Apollo 8 had its own TV show; the crew elected to go on live, despite the fact that Frank Borman had announced earlier that he had an upset stomach and that both Lovell and Anders were feeling nauseated. But the mood was cheerful as Frank announced: "This transmission is coming to you approximately halfway between the moon and the earth. We have been thirty-one hours and about twenty minutes into the flight. We have less than forty hours left to go to the moon."

A blue bank of computers in Mission Control showed them to be exactly 116,658.3 nautical miles from earth and proceeding away from the center of earth mass at precisely 4,794 feet per second, on course and on trajectory.

Later in the transmission, Jim Lovell flashed a bearded, guileless, weightless grin as he said, "Happy birthday, Mother."

Along with astronaut physician Dr. Charles Berry, other NASA personnel and members of the press, I watched the Apollo 8 television on the huge screen on the stage of the MSC auditorium. Now Dr. Berry leaned forward and made an unprecedented medical diagnosis.

"It is," he announced quietly, "reassuring to see this picture. I would doubt they are having much in the way of nausea at this moment. I think they are getting well." Never before had a bedside manner been exhibited so far from the patient.

After the brief show, Apollo 8 glided on silently, a microscopic dot of life ever broadening its excursion across the cosmic void.

On Christmas Eve, the worldwide television networks zeroed in for the second time on the tiny spacecraft antenna. The crew showed the earth a fantastic color picture of itself, a brown and blue, cloud-frosted planet serenely sailing through the dark ocean of noncircumscribed space. Said Lovell, "You are looking at yourselves at one hundred and eighty thousand miles out in space. Frank, what I keep imagining is, if I am some lonely traveler from another plant, what would I think of the earth at this altitude? Whether I think it would be inhabited or not."

The ground butted in: "Don't see anybody waving. Is that what you're saying?"

LOVELL: I was just kind of curious if I would land on the blue or the brown part of the earth.

BORMAN: You'd better hope it's the blue part.

Soon after they turned off their TV cameras, Borman, Lovell and Anders passed over the hill, or the point where the gravity of the earth and moon are equal. At this point, they ended their long climb out and became the first men to fall toward another celestial body. Although their ports were not positioned to see it at first, the moon loomed ahead of them like some gray and ghostly pumpkin, growing ever larger.

The time was approaching for the most critical decision of the mission: whether or not they would commit themselves for lunar orbit insertion, or LOI, in which the burn of the service module engine would try to place them in orbit around the moon.

At this dramatic moment of Christmas Eve when the planet seemed so peaceful to the crew of Apollo 8, one of earth's incredible ironies was taking place on a tiny portion of the brown and blue planet. Far below them, on a bridge in Korea, the haggard captain of another type of craft, Commander Lloyd Bucher, led a file of eighty-two weary men, victims of a quarrel on earth, into South Korea and freedom.

"Apollo 8, this is Houston at sixty-eight zero four.

You are go for LOI. . . . You are riding the best bird we can find. . . . We'll see you on the other side."

"Thanks a lot, troops," said Bill Anders. "See you on the other side."

Now as the spacecraft passed slowly behind the great curving crescent of the lonely perimeter of the moon, Dr. Berry, sitting comfortably in Mission Control, noted Frank Borman's heart rate beginning to rise. It peaked at 130 beats per minute, exactly matching his peak at liftoff.

"We've had a loss of signal with Apollo 8," the ground announced. A crawling, incommunicable, incredible blackout span of behind-the-moon time now began. The silence was ponderable and profound. Did it fire? Did it fire correctly? There was no way of knowing. Silence in Mission Control, in the massive Greenbelt, Maryland, tracking center, at Kennedy and at satellite tracking stations around the world — silence that was not a coffee break. The moon was a wall between the cradle and its venturesome earthlings. At precisely 69 hours, 33 minutes into the mission, before any voice could be heard from space, a small white light, called the DDD light, suddenly brightened on a key console in Mission Control. Computers thus told the light and the world that they had picked up acquisition signal.

"We've got it! We've got it! Apollo 8 is now in lunar orbit. There is a cheer now in this room. This is Apollo Control Houston, switching now to the voice of Jim Lovell."

Lovell first transmitted essential data, then Apollo Control eagerly butted in, "What does the ol' moon look like from sixty miles? Over."

"Okay, Houston," Lovell replied. "The moon is essentially gray, no color. Looks like plaster of Paris or sort of grayish beach sand."

He was giving an eyewitness account of a splendid journey down a line between the Foaming Sea, on his right, and on his left side the Sea of Fertility, the small crater Gutenberg and the Pyrenees Mountains.

"We can see quite a bit of detail. The craters are all rounded off . . . There's quite a few of them. Some of them are newer. Many of them look like — especially the round ones — look as if they were hit by meteorites or projectiles of some sort."

Two hours later, on the second pass, Bill Anders pointed the TV camera at what he called "whitish-gray dirty beach sand with lots of footprints in it." And — overbright at first but with a visible patina of circles and ripples — the ancient, crinkled face of the moon appeared to men on earth through the electronic legerdemain of television. Here perhaps was the Rosetta stone of the solar system, the missing billion years in the earth's past, tracking slowly beneath the lunar pioneers like a milky round embryo.

In between the front sides of two orbits, I talked briefly with a friend, Dick Hanrahan of IBM, who had temporarily left his console for a breath of air. Dick was in charge of Apollo Control's real-time computer complex. He showed his enormous responsibility in his red-eyed earnestness.

"I know each man feels we're doing something that man has wanted to do for centuries, but this is not an adventure for us yet. It's work. No black magic."

He spoke with the cautious optimism of a man who was watching lots of Sandy Koufaxes and Bob Gibsons show no sign of pain or tiring as they pitched the seventh inning of a no-hitter.

Three hours later, I spotted Dr. Charles Berry walking into a store across the street from the Manned Spacecraft Center. Apparently satisfied that his men at the moon, now past the halfway point, no longer needed medical advice, he calmly bought his wife a red wool suit for Christmas.

As I headed back for the press room, I happened upon one of those sights that could hardly be believed at first. It was two and a half hours before midnight and Christmas. The brightly growing moon, which looked like no other moon I had ever beheld, rested precisely above the flagpole in front of the MSC headquarters building. At the top of the pole, the spot-lighted flag moved gently in the night breeze. This is the only permissible display in the entire world of the American flag after dark. By custom, it flies at MSC as long as astronauts fly, as long as they are aloft in a realm that knows either a different day-night cycle, or none at all.

As I entered the press room, Frank Borman's tired voice appeared to come out of the walls and ceiling.

"The moon," he was saying, "is a different thing to each one of us. I know my own impression is that it's a vast, lonely, forbidding-type existence, like spans of nothing. It looks rather like clouds and clouds of pumice stone." Sometime later, a sleepy voice from the moon said, almost as a recitation, "And from the crew of

Apollo 8, we pause with good night, good luck, and God bless all of you — all of you on the good earth."

Still later that night, another friend of mine, a motion picture writer and producer named Don Wiseman, walked into the press room. It was nearly deserted and he was looking for a prevailing mood or theme for a motion picture on the flight he had yet to write. I had seen him drifting restlessly in and out for the past several days. Since he worked with and knew all three astronauts intimately, he immediately recognized Borman's clear voice coming out of the ceiling as Borman chatted, almost idly, with Jerry Carr in Mission Control. Lovell and Anders slept the sleep of the exhausted as their spacecraft slowly tracked around the moon.

"What's the weather like down there?" Borman asked in a casual tone that Wiseman thought had more than a hint of loneliness in it. Carr said it was a pretty night and that the moon was out.

"A nice time for Christmas," Borman said sleepily. "Nice weather for Christmas."

Wiseman's eyes lighted up. "That's the theme I've been looking for," he told me. "It's basically a mood picture. Here are three men, three ordinary family men sounding casual and maybe even corny, and feeling lonely at times right in the middle of a truly epic journey of modern man. And there is nothing wrong with that kind of corn, anyway. And here they are, at a time we need it most, giving us a mission that captures the human spirit and reminds us all of what man is or, maybe, what he should be or can be." He sat down and began to write.

Like Dick Hanrahan, he, too, was being drawn into the mood of that memorable Christmas night.

At ten minutes into Christmas Day on Apollo 8's twentieth revolution, the main engine, unheard and unrecorded on earth, was fired behind the moon. The mood was not that of a coffee break, until nine minutes later when radio contact was suddenly regained. Seconds later, amid cheers, Jim Lovell said cheerfully, "Houston, please be informed there is a Santa Claus . . . The burn was good."

"Roger, affirmative. You're the best ones to know."

Apollo 8 was now coasting on a return trajectory to earth. It was during this day that Borman, Lovell and Anders took turns reading from the Book of Genesis.

Later, Borman said, "I think I must have the feeling that the travelers in the old sailing ships used to have. Going on a very long voyage away from home, and now we're headed back. . . . And I have the feeling of being proud of the trip, but still happy to be going back home and back to home port."

Thursday, December 26, was the quietest day of the mission as the bone-tired crew sacked out.

"We are happy to report," said Borman in one wakeful moment, "that the earth is getting larger."

So incredibly accurate were all maneuvers that two of three scheduled midcourse corrections were eliminated.

On the morning of December 27, the three couriers from near the moon, unspacesuited, unhelmeted, began hitting molecules of hydrogen, nitrogen and oxygen at a speed of 24,530 miles per hour and at a pre-plotted angle

*The LOI burn of Apollo 8*

of precisely 6.43 degrees. Outside the simple core that was all that was left of the Apollo 8 train, the heat quickly rose to 5,000 degrees Fahrenheit.

At this instant, Captain Jake Marcum flying Pan American Airways' Flight 811 from Honolulu to Sidney, Australia pointed to an incandescent bolt burning downward into the dense, dark sky. Below the plane and the flaming spacecraft, the carrier *Yorktown*, 1,045 miles from Honolulu, gently rose and fell on five-foot swells. Television showed the deck scene as a moist tropical breeze fluttered the white uniforms of sailors gazing aloft. Seven minutes later, a lumbering C–130 aircraft forty-five miles from *Yorktown* reported a visual sighting on Apollo 8's flashing strobe lights. Two minutes later, *Yorktown* itself saw the flashing lights, and big brute helicopters homed in immediately on the Apollo parachutes. Incredibly, Apollo 8 drifted above the giant carrier. At exactly 147 hours after liftoff, the still hot spacecraft sizzled into the Pacific as the parachutes fell off into the sea.

"We are in real good shape, Houston," said Jim Lovell.

Because of the swells, it was some eighty-four minutes before the last astronaut was safely hoisted into the helicopter. Only minutes later one of the three frogmen who assisted the men and who were still in the water, Robe Coggin, spotted a ten-foot white-tipped Pacific shark circling nearby. This primitive earth denizen had apparently witnessed the return from the moon.

"We got into those hoist baskets real quick," Coggin recalled later.

At 12:20 eastern standard time, recovery helicopter number three touched down on *Yorktown*'s deck against a pink, blue and green Pacific dawn. Seconds later, three grinning men — white-suited in coveralls, wobbly and slightly unbalanced by the breeze — stepped gingerly down on a solid, flat, 1-g deck. Frank Borman, Jim Lovell and Bill Anders, lately of the distant moon, were happily reunited with their own kind, back on the planet earth.

It was several weeks before I had a chance to talk with the lunar astronauts in private. In the meantime, Don Wiseman finished his film, which was jetted to Washington for a private screening by President Nixon, and the astronauts had been hailed and cheered and showered with multiple honors.

My wife and I met Jim Lovell in his home on Lazywood Lane, and he talked eagerly about the flight as he sat on his living room couch. I asked him if his journey had in any way changed his view of life on earth.

"A lunar voyage," he replied, "can't help but give the traveler an awareness of where he stands in the universe. We have, of course, been earth centered; our impressions revolve around what we can see from the surface of the earth. When you get two hundred and forty thousand miles away, which is not very far in terms of the solar system, you see how small this earth really is. It's just a little body orbiting a medium-sized star that happens to be stuck in one corner of a rather small galaxy.

"From out there, it's difficult to understand the reason behind all the problems we have on earth. They don't seem real. When we see ourselves as some other traveler might first see us, you wonder why it is we can't live as peacefully as our small blue world looks from afar."

Frank Borman shared much the same view, although he expressed it differently. When I met with him in his office, shortly after his return from a hero's welcome in all the capitals of Western Europe, he closed the door so we could talk privately. He told me first how before the flight, the crew had difficulty deciding what they would read back to earth from the moon.

"After much discussion and careful thought," he said, "we decided that perhaps the first ten verses of Genesis would adequately relay our emotion. So we typed the ten verses on the flight plan and took off, hoping people would be able to relate to them."

"What reaction have you had?" I asked him.

"A few people were concerned because we did read from the Bible on what they considered to be public property and a public ride, so to speak; but the overall response to date, especially from our mail, has been something like a thousand-to-one in favor of what we did."

Later, I asked him about his feelings while circling the moon and looking back at earth. As he leaned back in his chair, his manner was thoughtful. He spoke slowly — but he was very sure of his words.

"When you look at our earth from two hundred and forty thousand miles away, especially over a horizon that has been bombarded for eons, you see that our planet is the only thing in the universe that has any color in it. You don't know whether the blue is water or the blue is land. You don't really know whether it's inhabited or not. Yet you know there is life there. And preserving that life seems very, very important.

"The overwhelming impression of the people of Europe was this view that we got of earth. They seemed intently interested in the fact that there are really no barriers. They responded to the fact that we are really riders on the earth together. And we share such a beautiful planet. It's small and beautiful and fragile.

"Now I'm not naïve enough to think that things like exploring the moon are going to take away the conflicts that exist on earth, but it helps give us a significant and common point of view. We on earth really have much more in common than we have in separation. Earth isn't really very big. The atmosphere seems so big to us here, but half of it is gone above three miles. To Europeans and Americans both, the overwhelming wonderment is why in the world we can't appreciate what we have. And how we can approve of one another and really co-exist on a peaceful level. And, of course, the answers are in each one of us. The question is how do we get them out? If by leaving the earth we can help bring these forth, then the journey is one the world needs."

## 9

# The Amazing LEM-
# Bug Proves Itself

*I don't know if you've ever seen a tissue paper spacecraft
before, but this thing sure looks the part.*
— ASTRONAUT JAMES McDIVITT

HAD NO MORE FLIGHTS to the moon been planned to follow the circumlunar flight of Apollo 8, a significant part
of man's emotional and migratory need to fly to the
moon would have been satisfied and fulfilled. Taken by
itself, however, Apollo 8 satisfied very little of man's
scientific or intellectual curiosity. It was intended prima-
rily as a reconnaissance flight for the future lunar landings which would return with a cargo of priceless lunar
lodestone. As Jim Lovell said afterward, "Orbiting the
moon sixty miles above its surface was a great experience,
but our goal is to go all the way down. And the last sixty
miles are the hardest."

The only way Apollo 8 could have reached the moon
— and such a landing as a matter of fact was a remote
possibility viewed with some concern before the flight —
would have been to crash there. The reason for this, of
course, was that Apollo 8 carried no equipment capable

of landing on or lifting off the moon's surface. The rocket train did not include one of the most remarkable means of human transportation ever devised: LEM was not attached.

Originally called the lunar excursion module and later shortened to lunar module, it was always called LEM, the bug, the LEM-bug or the spider by astronauts and engineers. The first time I ever saw the amazing LEM-bug was in moonlight. I had heard that the first full-sized replica had arrived in Houston and had been placed on the acre of ground especially prepared to look like the moon's surface. Visitors to the Manned Spacecraft Center unfortunately never see this strange-looking plot of cinder rock and pumice stone that has been gouged out with small and large craters. When it was first constructed it had neither fence nor guards, and when I drove out one night in my car to see LEM, I came upon this eerily realistic make-believe moon suddenly, and entirely alone. As I got out of the car, there was bug-eyed LEM perched in the slanting light of the moon as if it had recently come from the black void of the sky itself. As I walked slowly toward it, my shoes crunched against the slippery cinders. To my left was an irregular mound of white pumice powder which shone like a grassless sand dune in the moonlight. I could not resist scrambling up to its crest for a better view of LEM. As I climbed, my footsteps implanted themselves in powder as fine as dry snow. The bug sat, slightly askew, with its four spindly and saucer-footed legs implanted near a crater fully seventeen feet deep.

One leg had a ladder running up to its "front porch"

*Replica of the LEM on simulated lunar surface*

and hatch, which looked like a nose. Above the nose a
pair of triangular window ports looked like eyes. From
its head and sides jutted jet pods and Martian-looking an-
tennas. As I climbed up the ladder and stood on the
porch, I saw the United States flag on LEM's glowing
flanks. Not a sound could be heard anywhere on that acre
of lunarscape. What boy in America would not like to
have stood there just as the young Herman Melville,
who later wrote *Moby Dick*, must have stood on the
prow of his first whaling vessel as it carried him out of
Gloucester harbor? For a moment, the view and the feel-

ing was that of a realm more mysterious and remote than the sea itself.

But when I climbed down and crunched back across the cinders, the landscape did not seem like the moon at all. Night cloud shadows flowed across the mound of pumice and darkened the pits of craters. Rolling Texas tumbleweeds brushed against my legs. Some of the craters, I now noticed, had water in them, and a mosquito stung my cheek. Mosquitoes on the moon? I had to laugh at that.

LEM came by its boxy, ungainly look because, unlike streamlined Mercury, Gemini or the Apollo command module, it was not designed to fly in the air at all. At its birthplace on earth before the LEM is pressurized, it looks almost as frail as an aluminum balloon. It relates to nothing known, since it was not made for this planet. It was to be transported away from earth tucked and folded inside Saturn like an insect in a dark cocoon. Only after it reached its intended element of space was it to be drawn out, turned around, linked up and finally allowed to unfold its delicate moon legs in the bright sunlight.

Its main purpose was to carry two men down to the moon, let them out, let them in, then, shucking its bottom half, blast upward to ferry men and cargo to the command ship. Once lunar rendezvous and docking was accomplished, men and cargo deserted it. At this point, LEM became useless, unless — under rare circumstances — it was needed as a "lifeboat." Under normal circumstances it would be abandoned near the moon. No museum save the cosmos would ever hold LEM. The vehicle was like the male bee that follows the queen high in the sky, mates, dies and apparently disappears.

For its brief but vital function, LEM had to be built by men nearly as carefully and reliably as nature built the bee.

In a way, Apollo 9 was the first flight scheduled to carry a crew of four: Jim McDivitt, Russell Schweickart, David Scott and the ingenious robot of over a million parts which was code-named *Spider*. *Spider*, in fact, received far more pre-flight nursing and grooming than did any of the human crew. *Spider*'s inventors — who if assembled could fill a huge laboratory — secured their creation in its cocoon and pronounced it ready in February 1969.

Because of the intricacies of the planned tests in earth orbit and the magnitude of the data the human crew had to transmit to radio receiving stations during intermittent contact with earth, Jim McDivitt said at one point prior to flight, "There is so much information you really have to be careful what you do with it. You are almost overwhelmed by the amount of information you have to handle."

Jim McDivitt had been a classmate at the University of Michigan of Ed White, one of the astronauts killed in the Apollo fire, and had known Frank Borman and Tom Stafford at a special Air Force pilot's school. He had also flown with Neil Armstrong at Edwards Air Force Base. McDivitt was extremely informal and easygoing, a nice guy who never finished last in anything. A veteran of 145 fighter missions in Korea, he had earned an advanced degree in aeronautical engineering and was selected to be one of the choice group of X–15 test pilots. McDivitt's manner of talking was to use simple words with no intellectual pretensions and — like a lot of experienced pilots — to understate his own feelings and emotions. He seemed uncomplicated only to those who accepted his language for the complete man.

Red-haired and youthful-looking Rusty Schweickart had waited patiently for twenty-eight months for his first flight. When he became an astronaut, he was, at thirty-one, the youngest astronaut in his class, but he had impressive credentials, including a master's degree from MIT. As soon as he learned that he was scheduled for a space walk in Apollo 9, he started training himself, using a spring steel hand exerciser to strengthen his hands and arms.

Dave Scott, like Frank Borman, had been plagued with illness as a child but the effects did not linger. The son of an Army Air Corps pilot (a brigadier general) from San Antonio, Scott graduated fifth in his class at West Point and then became an Air Force pilot himself. At six feet and 175 pounds, he looks like and is one of the strongest of the astronauts. He has rugged features and walks with an erect military bearing.

Liftoff on the vital check-out flight of Apollo 9 came on the morning of March 3. After successfully reaching earth orbit, the crew fired small thrusters to detach the command ship, *Gumdrop*, from its train, carefully turned it around and aimed its ten-inch probe at the cone-shaped receptacle of *Spider*, still snuggled in its garage. The two craft touched and mated. *Spider* then was pushed out into the element for which it was designed when McDivitt flipped a switch that enabled springs to push LEM away from the rocket stage.

In a series of four firings spread over two days, the Apollo 9 crew went successively into higher and more durable orbits until their high point of orbit was about three hundred miles. On the last firing McDivitt even caused the burning engine to move back and forth to see how strong the link was between the two craft.

"You can feel the whole thing shake and vibrate," Scott informed the ground, "but it's pretty solid."

Everything was now set for the delicate crew transfer to LEM. Scott performed the chore work: removing the docking mechanism from the tunnel, plugging in electrical connections and equalizing the pressure between the two spaceships. Then Rusty Schweickart, whose continuing nausea had just caused him to vomit, pulled himself through the 32-inch-diameter transfer tunnel into *Spider*. There, he vomited again. He was joined about an hour later by McDivitt, and together they checked out *Spider*'s numerous systems for about eight hours. Fortunately, no serious problems developed, and the two men were clear to test *Spider*'s engine while it was still coupled to *Gumdrop*.

"*Spider* and *Gumdrop*," said the ground, "you are go for the docked DPS burn."

"Roger . . . All clear and ignition . . . Firing the throttle forty percent . . . Going down to ten percent . . . Back up to forty percent . . ."

They were now satisfied they could go ahead with the planned space walk and vital rendezvous attempt as scheduled but, first, McDivitt had a message.

"Listen, I'm going to get something to eat. All I've had

so far is a little bag of fruit salad and I'm about to starve to death."

The next day McDivitt and Rusty returned to *Spider* for the first test of the lunar portable life support system (called the PLSS) and the suit to be worn on the moon. Rusty Schweickart now became a sort of separate one-man spacecraft, code-named *Red Rover*, as he opened *Spider*'s hatch and stepped out onto the front porch.

"Boy oh boy, what a view!" he exclaimed.

After a moment he said to Scott, "Dave, come on out . . . wherever you are."

The two men working together outside *Spider* and *Gumdrop* retrieved experimental packages and pulled themselves along especially provided handrails. The required outside duties and exertions showed the lunar suit assembly to be sound.

On the next day, the fifth day in space, came the most significant test of all. McDivitt and Rusty in *Spider* started to undock from Scott in *Gumdrop*. But after Scott punched the button, they remained hung up.

"Oh oh," said Scott, "we didn't release."

He pressed the button harder.

"Okay," he radioed *Spider*, "you're free."

They drifted for an hour close together, then *Spider* fired up small thrusters that caused it to move off by itself through space. Under McDivitt's control, the amazing LEM-bug moved into a different orbit from *Gumdrop*'s. Finally, it was about one hundred miles away, far out of sight of the mother ship. Now with the support of Mission Control and onboard computers, Mc-

Divitt and Schweickart had the task of locating Scott and rejoining him. First, they pressed the button to fire up their engine.

"It's a good burn, Dave," McDivitt said.

Each of several burns now represented a firing rehearsal for lunar rendezvous and docking, but to the men on board *Spider*, the burns were not rehearsal for anything. They were their only means of getting back to *Gumdrop* and to earth. If they could not rendezvous, they could never return to earth, since their delicate *Spider* had no heat shield. They knew that if their maneuvers were anything but perfect, they would be marooned in space.

The suspenseful operation took six long hours. When Scott finally caught sight of *Spider* it was apparent that one of the two spacecraft had inverted itself during their separation.

"You are upside down," Scott radioed McDivitt.

McDivitt corrected him with a fine point of scientific observation. "One of us isn't right side up," he said.

As McDivitt flipflopped his craft and edged closer, Scott commented, "You're the biggest, friendliest, funniest-looking spider I've ever seen."

McDivitt had some unexpected difficulty lining up his probe precisely toward the command ship's waiting receptacle. This was because sunlight reflected off the sighting device on LEM's docking window — a contingency that had been impossible to test on the ground.

"You ought to go forward and to your right a little bit relative to your body," Scott told him.

"Somehow, oh, I see it. There it is. There," McDivitt said.

"Keep coming. Almost there. Okay, you are about there . . . I have capture."

As they linked and locked together, an audible and confirming tone sounded in each spacecraft.

Said McDivitt, "I haven't heard a song that good for a long time . . . Man, when I take a break, I'm going to bed for three days."

It had been a full and rewarding five days. *Spider* had performed excellently. Now, the two crews rejoined, and it was time to say good-bye to their amazing LEM-bug. They separated, then automatically ignited LEM's descent engine. It would burn until its propellants ran out.

The men of Apollo 9 watched as their crewless bug sped away. Perhaps no one would ever see it again.

"It's really moving out," Rusty said. "I hope I didn't forget anything important . . . He's sure a long ways away."

Apollo 9's last five days settled into a routine of picture taking and observations with an occasional burn to refine their orbit. Things were so quiet that a NASA official commented at one point, "The big events of today are the sleep cycle and the wake-up period." The primary purpose of the extra days was to test thoroughly all the Apollo systems.

The pictures taken — both stills and motion pictures — were to turn out to be one of the most remarkable documentations of space ever made. When Apollo 9 reentered the atmosphere on March 13, the crew members'

*"You're the biggest, friendliest, funniest-looking spider I've ever seen"*

16-mm Maurer movie camera recorded the violence of air impact and braking. An orange-yellow glow completely engulfed the spaceship. Individual chunks of incandescence tore off their honeycombed heat shield and streaked by their window ports. Parachute shroud lines lashed crazily in the wind. Then the three great orange and white main chutes opened and bobbed back and forth in view of the camera lens.

A worldwide TV audience also had a clear picture of the descending spacecraft as it drifted out of the Atlantic cloud cover near Grand Turk Island in the Bahamas and splashdowned just three miles from the carrier *Guadalcanal*. Because of heavy seas near the original landing point off Bermuda, the crew had to stay up one more orbit so a shift in landing zones could be made. After splashdown, with the mission all but over, the three men had an unusual amount of difficulty during the hoisting operation from the sea to the helicopters. First, the draft from the helicopter roters blew Apollo and its floating rafts away from the dangling "cage" intended to hoist the astronauts. After ten misses, Scott finally clambered in. Then Rusty was dragged through the water as he tried to climb in. The wind picked McDivitt's raft up and turned it over. McDivitt was thoroughly dunked and had to clamber into Apollo's flotation collar for safety. Finally, he grabbed the swinging cage in desperation and was lifted to safety.

The success of the first LEM of Apollo 9 was such that a number of NASA officials seriously considered that the mission of Apollo 10 — already planned as a circumlunar flight — be changed to permit an actual landing attempt.

But more cautious experts argued that LEM needed additional check-out in the actual lunar environment before undertaking the potentially hazardous landing.

A primary cause of concern was the strange variations in lunar gravity found on the Apollo 8 flight. Post-flight analysis showed that at some points Apollo 8 had been up to three miles behind and up to 2,500 feet up or down from its calculated position in lunar orbit. The cause of these orbital disturbances was thought to be the presence of mascons, mysterious and dense concentrations of mass just below the moon's surface. Were these remnants of great iron meteors? Or something else? What effect would they have on the actual lunar landing missions and on the lunar gravity rendezvous maneuvers between LEM and the command ship? In NASA's opinion, there were too many unknowns. The decision was made that Apollo 10 would not attempt to land, but would carry LEM to the moon to test it near but not on the surface.

Selected to fly in Apollo 10 was the backup crew of Apollo 7. Thomas P. Stafford, a veteran of two Gemini flights, was named commander of Apollo 10; John W. Young, also a veteran of two Gemini flights, was named pilot of the command ship and navigator; and Eugene A. Cernan, who had flown before with Stafford, was selected as the LEM pilot. It was the first U.S. space crew made up entirely of men who had been in space before. Their mission: check out all Apollo systems in the lunar environment, fly and check out LEM within less than ten miles of the target moon, and scout the primary Apollo 11 landing zone.

Stafford had suffered through so many long on-the-pad delays in Gemini that someone once said he had more time on the pad than some astronauts had in orbit.

"One thing you can count on this time," he said. "I'm going to get off on time."

John Young, who lived across the street from the Staffords, had green eyes and was quick with a laugh or dry pun. His original home was in Orlando, Florida, just sixty-five miles from the space port at Cape Kennedy. His biggest mission responsibility would be in his navigation skill as he back-stopped every move Stafford and Cernan would make as they approached within 50,000 feet of the moon. Throughout the long pre-flight training, Young showed a willingness to excel in any assignment given him.

Before the flight, Young's hopes were high, but he commented at one point, "There are three hundred and seventy things that can go wrong to prevent us from accomplishing our mission."

An English reporter asked Young why all the vital burns and maneuvers took place on the moon's backside, beyond the range of radio contact. Is it an insurmountable problem, he wanted to know, to have these maneuvers take place on the front side?

"It's an insurmountable problem, all right," Young replied. "You ought to talk to that guy Kepler."

Young was referring to the brilliant astronomer Johannes Kepler, who first formulated the laws of planetary motion.

Eugene Cernan, thirty-five, was, of all members of the crew, a casting director's choice of what an astronaut should look like. He came into the astronaut program at the top of the permitted height — exactly six feet. His deep-set blue eyes and even, masculine facial features, topped by a crewcut of gray-flecked brown hair, gave him a rugged, handsome look. Astrologist Jeanne Dixon had once predicted that Cernan "would startle the world with one of his ideas," but Cernan was the kind of man who paid more attention to what his former pastor in Chicago said. Cernan was very serious about space and was constantly selling the national need for a vigorous space program.

Before the Apollo 10 flight, when NASA announced that it would include "several hours" of color TV, Cernan commented, "Maybe TV is one way we can pay back the American taxpayer for his support of the Apollo moon program. We want to share some of the things we expect to see. I think this program belongs to a lot of people."

To lessen the chances that crew illness such as had plagued previous Apollo flights would occur on Apollo 10, NASA took extraordinary precautions not only to avoid sending another contagious virus into space but also to moderate the effects of motion sickness. Until Apollo, the Russians had been concerned that their cosmonauts got sick in space while our Mercury and Gemini pilots did not, and now the prevailing theory was that the extra room for body movement available in the Russian spacecraft and in Apollo contributed to motion sickness. It was this which was believed to have caused Rusty Schweickart's upset stomach. Since Frank Borman and others felt that some pills they had taken in flight had worsened rather than aided their general condition, Stafford, Young and Cernan were tested in advance on every item in the Apollo 10 medical kit. None suffered ill effects on the ground. In addition, Dr. Berry prescribed certain head movement exercises which he believed would speed up the adaptation to the weightless state and avoid serious motion sickness. Periodically, each astronaut was to nod his head on the count of "one-two" in four directions, up, down, left and right.

The ninety-three-hour countdown began in mid-May 1969. The total mission time scheduled was eight days, including sixty-one hours and thirty-five minutes in lunar orbit, three times as long as in Apollo 8. The radio and television code names were taken from the popular Charles Schulz comic strip *Peanuts*. The command module would be called *Charlie Brown* and LEM would be called *Snoopy*. Snoopy was popular with astronauts and had earlier appeared on safety posters displayed after the Apollo fire.

For a while it appeared that Tom Stafford's launch delay jinx was going to work again. Thousands of gallons of high grade kerosene propellant poured out the bottom of the massive Saturn rocket while it awaited final day launch preparations. When this human error was determined not to have caused any problems, a minor technical detail threatened to abort the launch.

To Stafford's great relief, however, liftoff from the pad 39A launch platform, which is as large as a baseball diamond, occurred on schedule on the Sunday morning of May 18.

"Just like old times. It's beautiful out there," Stafford said.

The TLI burn also occurred on schedule. During the first mating between *Charlie Brown* and *Snoopy*, the world got a breathtaking view via live color television as a newly developed camera focused on *Snoopy* 4,120 miles above the earth. Then the camera turned toward the blue, brown and white planet earth, set like a gem in the black sky. By the time the crew turned in that night they were over 77,000 miles from home.

On the next day no illness yet had been reported. The new head exercises seemed to be working. Once when Stafford started to drink water, he gulped a mouthful of chlorinated water instead. Through a ground error, the crew had left a valve open which permitted the chlorine to build up in the drinking tube. The astronauts also had to drink some troublesome hydrogen bubbles, a product of their fuel cells, in their water, and the bubbles caused uncomfortable stomach gas. On the positive side, their diet included bread, which had not been aboard a spacecraft since John Young smuggled a corned beef sandwich aboard the first Gemini flight in 1965. To keep the bread from drying out in the 100 percent oxygen atmosphere, it had been saturated with nitrogen which — as the local grocery store ought to find out — keeps bread fresh for up to two weeks.

For three and a half days, interspersed with vividly colorful televised pictures, Stafford, Young and Cernan coasted closer to their target. On May 21, the lunar orbit insertion burn was successful.

Shortly after going into lunar orbit, however, a potentially serious problem developed. When Tom Stafford started to crawl through the tunnel into LEM, he was surprised to see snowlike pieces of material floating around the tunnel. He discovered then that the padding in LEM's hatch had ripped, apparently during pressurization, releasing the fiberglass insulation. It was no trouble to brush the substance aside, but, later, when they tried to depressurize the tunnel, nothing happened. It took some time to discover that some of the drifting fiberglass had plugged up a small air vent.

The next problem was not expected either. For some reason, *Snoopy* had twisted about three degrees at its juncture point with *Charlie Brown*. The ground examined this new problem and, just before Apollo 10 disappeared behind the moon, reported to the crew that if the twist went as much as six degrees, undocking was not advised. No one knew for long moments what had happened behind the moon.

What was happening, however, was a great joy to Stafford and Cernan. They were undocked and were temporarily "keeping station" beside Young in *Charlie Brown*.

"Keep up the good work, boys," Young radioed to them. "You will never know how big this thing looks when there ain't nobody in it but one guy."

In the comic strip, Snoopy is a comical, flop-eared beagle dog who forever dreams of glorious exploits, such as dueling the Red Baron, the greatest German pilot of World War I, in aerial combat. Now his namesake was to have a real exploit, and it was dangerous. Just three extra seconds of thrust could cause *Snoopy* to head for a crash on the moon.

Stafford fired *Snoopy*'s descent rocket. The LEM-bug started down in a long sweeping arc toward Apollo 11's intended landing site. LEM came on down to about 100,-000 feet, traveling like a supersonic lunar transport across the desolate lunarscape.

"I tell you we're down here where we can touch the top of some of the hills," Cernan said.

Still they came on down toward the eventual landing site. When they got down to 47,000 feet, about nine miles, Cernan could hardly contain himself.

"We're right there!" he exclaimed. "We're right over it! I'm telling you we are low. We're close, baby. This is it!"

Said Stafford wistfully, "I just wish we could stay."

*Snoopy* had finally had his moment of glory, down in the lunar wilderness, among the peaks, valleys, plains, craters and sinuous rills, which not even the cat next door had ever seen. But another trial yet remained. Just after the descent stage, or lower half, of *Snoopy* was jettisoned, it appeared for a moment as if the Red Baron had finally drilled them.

"Son of a bitch," Cernan suddenly yelled. "Something is wrong with the gyro." As *Snoopy* pitched, dipped and yawed crazily, Cernan's heart rate went from 67 beats to 129. It took Tom Stafford over a minute to bring his bucking spacecraft under control.

Cernan said solemnly, "I don't know what that was, baby, but that was something. I thought we were wobbling all over the skies."

The difficulty turned out to have been due to a human error, a switch setting somehow omitted from the checklist. The crew was shaken, but the danger appeared to have passed.

After LEM's ascent engine was fired, the men went back around the moon in a sweeping climbing curve that took them back toward lonely John Young. When they came out on the other side, the eastern edge of the moon, Stafford's Oklahoma accent summed it up: "We is going," he told Charlie Duke in Mission Control. "We is down among 'em, Charlie."

Now, the final rendezvous burn of the smaller rockets was fired. LEM's thin, aluminum walls, which Jim McDivitt had once referred to as tissue paper, shook and rattled.

"If you wanted a LEM-simulated ride," Stafford said to John Young as they drew nearer, "let your kids get a big metal bowl on your head and beat on it with spoons."

After successful linkup, it was time to say good-bye to *Snoopy*. As its engine fired and it sped off alone looking for the eternal Red Baron, Cernan said, "God, I feel sort of bad about that because he's a pretty nice guy . . . He treated us pretty well today."

On its thirty-first and final revolution, on a morning the earth called Saturday, *Charlie Brown*'s propulsion engine gave the reunited crew the big push back toward home, exactly 246,154 miles away.

As they receded from the moon, Stafford, who had insisted from the beginning on bringing color television along, kept his camera trained on the moon for long minutes. People on earth thus saw the "Queen of Night," live and dead, as it appeared full screen in all its elemental privacy.

"I tell you," Cernan philosophized, "this satellite of ours — this moon of ours — had a rough beginning somewhere back there."

Coming home, the astronauts shaved. This apparently unremarkable action has a history behind it. Shaving in space, some NASA earth walkers had long believed, would be impossible. Little hair bits would float all over the place fouling up delicate electronic gear. NASA even spent precious research money on a sort of combination electric shaver and vacuum cleaner. But the astronauts did it the hard way. They bought a forty-nine-cent tube of brushless shaving cream at a Cape Kennedy drugstore, spread it on their faces and scraped off their fuzz with an old-fashioned safety razor. The hair bits stayed stuck in the goo and could be wiped off the razor with a paper towel. Thus the shaving bugaboo disappeared like that now ancient notion that a man in the weightless state could not drink water because it would stay in his gullet and choke him.

It was three clean-shaven men who, after the fifty-four-and-a-half-hour return voyage, splashed down in the Pacific near Pago Pago.

John Young radioed the nearby helicopter carrier *Princeton:* "Tell the medical officer to take a couple of aspirins and relax. We feel great."

Before the Apollo 10 flight Tom Stafford had said, "When the Apollo 11 astronauts hear our description and study our photographs, we want them to feel as if they had been there themselves." As it turned out — thanks to the crew, the Apollo systems and the amazing LEM-bug — that was about the way it was, except that nobody yet had gone those last important nine miles. And it was now up to LEM-bug number three to do just that. Within an hour after the Apollo 10 crew walked across *Princeton*'s deck, Dr. Thomas Paine, the NASA administrator, told reporters at Houston, "We know we can go to the moon. We will go to the moon. Tom Stafford, John Young and Gene Cernan have given us the final confidence to take this bold step."

Apollo 11 thus had the official "go" to shoot for the surface of the moon.

## 10

# Footprints on the Moon

*And don't tell me man doesn't belong out there. Man be-
longs wherever he wants to go — and he'll do plenty well
when he gets there.*

— Wernher von Braun

ON THE EVENING of Tuesday, July 15, 1969, the night
before the long-heralded launch of Apollo 11, I drove
alone into Cape Kennedy in a rented car. The car, I had
decided in advance, would also be my bed, if, indeed,
sleep were possible at all during any portion of that long
night.

I drove in on a splendid four-lane highway that ran
over a magnificent bridge spanning the Indian and Ba-
nana rivers. Back in 1956, when Cape Canaveral, as it
was then called, was a tightly guarded and entirely military rocket development center, the bridge I often traveled over had been rickety, and the highway had been a
thin strip of asphalt that in places was buckled and lumpy
on an insecure bed of shoreline sand. Now, thirteen years
later, the security was virtually all gone, and the facilities were the very best that a rich nation could provide.
The launch of the first men to land on the moon was to
be a showcase demonstration of what the most highly fo-

cused effort of twentieth-century technology could accomplish, and — as befitting to the citizens and taxpayers who had made it possible — it was to be a highly public affair. Everyone, from Congressmen to television comedians, had been invited. This fact was a source of pride, since the high visibility of our space program educated us to both our virtues and vices, our successes and our errors and, above all, our boldness and willingness to risk conspicuous failure in the fishbowl of publicity. But this publicity was also, unaccountably, a source of some sadness to me.

In the Fifties as I approached Cape Canaveral, I had eagerly strained from the elevation of the last bridge for my first view of the citadel of the Free World's rocketry. The sight of those first tall gantries jutting into the night sky like jeweled skyscrapers behind their rings of barbed wire and patrol boats symbolized the entire, fascinating emerging staging area for a totally new transportation system. The tall gantries of the skyline, often seen dimly through the shrouds of shoreline mist, were vivid and dramatic for what they already were. Their presence, insular though it was, meant that the rocket age was upon us. They were also fascinating for the promise they held. And in tomorrow's sunlight, a significant part of the promise would begin to be fulfilled as men for the first time would try to stand and walk on land that belonged to no nation on earth — nor to earth itself.

So as my car topped the last bridge, I strained again and was not disappointed. Only tiny red lights told where the other great towers were — for Atlases, for Titans, for Centaurs and Thors. These once mighty-sounding names were now dwarfed by the Goliath of pad 39A. There a phalanx of whitish-blue searchlights gave the moon launcher the appearance of a gleaming pillar of cavern quartz. The crisscrossing beams played out across the dark heavens in such a grand aurora that I wondered if the glow was visible from the moon itself.

I stopped first at NASA's press center to pick up my badge. In contrast to Canaveral's old press center, which was a single and not very efficient military office, the two-story NASA center looked like a modern airline terminal for a city of half a million people. Nearby were other evidences of abundance: the Cape Kennedy Hilton hotel, ablaze with lights and noisy with revelers, and the stark statement of the ultramodern IBM building.

I walked inside the garishly lighted and crowded press room a total stranger. I recognized no one, and no one recognized me. These reporters, photographers, minor government officials and clerks could all have been of a different country. On ranks of tables were the brochures, fact sheets, portfolios, photographs, diagrams and backgrounders expansively and expensively prepared by the host of aerospace corporations whose manifold services and hardware were involved in the flight. No one wanted his contribution to go unnoticed. I felt as uncomfortable as a stranger in a pool hall beseiged by sharks. I looked around again for a friend, saw none and left as quickly as I could to go down to the beach.

"There is magic in it," Herman Melville once wrote. "Let the most absentminded of men be plunged into his deepest reveries — stand that man on his legs, set his feet a-going, and he will lead you to water, if water there be in all that region."

But I did not go down to the beach just to see the water. I went to see the rocket standing on the particular patch of earth from where it would depart for the moon. I knew that tomorrow I would be near that patch, and now I wanted to see it from afar. On the south coast of England there is a place called Land's End. In the great days of sail, it was said, you could stand there and see the ships go over the horizon. Now I wanted to see Land's End in another sense — the place where a new kind of ship would not go over the horizon but would, if all went well, go straight up and entirely through it. "The longest journey is the journey upward," Dag Hammarskjold once said. I came to see the rocket in privacy and ended up seeing a considerable portion of America. At Port Canaveral's south jetty, there is a little corner of shoreline where I used to sit at night waiting for rockets to rise. There are dunes there covered with rustling thick-leaved sea grapes and tall sea oats whose linear base leaves arch gracefully back to earth. The wind moves their tips and etches little crescents and curlicues in the sand. Across the short, hard-packed coquina beach, you can hear the waves tumble among the jetty rocks and then splay out with a diminishing hiss over the wet sands. I went there now, but others were there before me.

As I drove in, friendly volunteer traffic cops directed me away from soft sand, around tent pegs, in and out among the bumpers and fenders of parked cars, pickup trucks, station wagons, campers, dune buggies, motor-cycles, travel buses, jalopies and plain establishment sedans.

I parked, got out and looked around; it must have been around midnight. Some were asleep in sleeping bags on the sand, in the backs of cars, or rolled in blankets on the roofs and the hoods of cars. Near me two bare feet projected out a rear car window. But other campers were still astir, their shadows jerking in the particular cold white light that Coleman lanterns give off. Car and portable radios were softly tuned to music or commentators giving countdown status.

I went down to the wet part of the beach. Couples sat or slept nearby on the dry sand, while some barefoot kids chased sand crabs in the now distant light of the Colemans. Turning to the north, I saw the big arc lights still pinpointing the moon rocket. I heard a radio announcer say that the countdown was on schedule. The air, the entire beach, seemed charged with suspense.

Walking back toward my car, I greeted a friendly-looking man sitting alone on a cooler under a tent flap. He was listening to a pocket radio.

"Where're you from?" I asked.

"Macon, Georgia," he replied. "They predicted there'd be a million people here. So I told my wife and the kids we'd make it a million and four."

I was glad now these people had found the south jetty. Going to the moon really meant something to these people. I felt better than I had felt that entire night.

I drove back and parked my car in an open field not far from the NASA press center. I climbed in the back seat and pulled a coat over me. But I didn't sleep much. I thought of the strange moon that night, the people on the beach, the waiting rocket, the old days, this bad thing about not seeing any friends. But mostly I thought about the astronauts. It was good to think about the men who were to make the journey while they were asleep and resting.

I had known Neil Armstrong since about 1963, not very well since I didn't see him often and there was a secret and guarded part of himself he held back from other people. As my friend Jim Maloney said before the flight, "They will remember him forever, but they will never know him well." Neil and I had sometimes worked on stories together. I had asked him questions, and he had given slow, thoughtful answers which he would later meticulously edit if I showed them to him before they appeared in print. He seemed very ambitious and wanted people to get just the right impression of him. He knew, of course, that NASA based major flight assignments partly on an astronaut's ability to communicate his "public personality," and he was very anxious to communicate properly to the public. One Christmas, I had bought some jars of rare tupelo honey to take around as presents to a few close astronaut friends. By the time my son and I got to the Armstrong house in El Lago — his first home that later burned — I was out of honey, but we went in anyway to say Merry Christmas. It was a mistake. Neil and his wife Jan were rather grimly cleaning house after a party. I had heard loud voices as I knocked and, once inside, there wasn't much to say. Neil was polite, but I felt I had interrupted an argument and left at the first opportunity.

I didn't go back into his house again until I took the first Ranger photographs, fresh from Pasadena, California, for him to see. I remember the careful, deliberate way he spread out the first close-up pictures of the moon's surface on his kitchen table. As he examined each one, a sharp light shone in his eyes that could have been either pleasure or a very intense order of want. I felt even then that Neil Armstrong desperately wanted the moon and that, perhaps, this was as it should be. No one would want to schedule an astronaut who didn't want very much to go there, whatever his reasons.

The known facts of Neil's life indicated that most of his drive was internal, beneath the surface. His teachers in Wapakoneta, Ohio, recall his early curiosity about aviation and space. He grew naturally into scouting and became an Eagle scout. He took flight lessons so early that he got a pilot's license at sixteen before he was legally old enough to obtain a driver's license. At nineteen, he became a Navy fighter pilot in Korea. After Korea, he worked briefly as a pilot and engineer at the Lewis Laboratory. Then he tried out for and won the right to go to Edwards Air Force Base, where such famed test pilots as Joe Walker, Scott Crossfield, Milton Thompson and Chuck Yeager lived and worked. When I was last at Edwards, I asked about Neil while lunching with two test pilots, Milton Thompson and Bruce Peterson, who knew him as an X–15 rocket plane pilot. They both spoke well of him. "Neil was a natural pilot," Milt

Thompson said. "He came out here in the first place because, with the Dyna-Soar program going, he thought this was the road to space. When NASA's manned spacecraft program sprang up suddenly, he thought about it awhile, then decided that was the place to be and put in his application."

As a Gemini pilot, Neil's skill was notable. Gemini 8, which he commanded, became the first spacecraft to dock with another object in space, the Agena rocket. But moments after the linkup, a serious emergency arose. One of the spacecraft thrusters stuck and started firing wide open, causing the two linked vehicles to spin and roll violently. Neil and his partner, David Scott, finally brought the near disaster to an end, but they used up so much fuel that they had to land early.

Later, Neil coolly responded to another near disaster in the lunar lander. To train astronauts to let down on the moon with rocket power only — without the help of props, wings or helicopter rotors — a special lunar lander training device called the flying bedstead was built. It was a formidable-looking maze of aluminum and steel built around a big gimboled central engine and a series of outboard thrusters. Armstrong was one of the first astronauts to attempt to fly it. One day while he was attempting to hover and control the tricky machine above a runway at nearby Ellington Air Force Base, it malfunctioned. Seconds before crashing, Neil hit the button of his ejection seat. The escape mechanism exploded him straight up, giving his parachute just enough time to open before he slammed against the hard ground.

Neil admitted that both these near disasters scared him,

but he said that he was ready to go again. This was one of the reasons NASA named him, a civilian, above two other crew members who were both Air Force lieutenant colonels and West Point graduates as commander of the Apollo 11 mission.

Lieutenant Colonel Edwin (Buzz) Aldrin was not told he was assigned to walk on the moon with Neil Armstrong until just a few days before the public announcement of January 9, 1969. His official title on the mission was lunar module commander. When Aldrin's class of astronauts was originally picked, observers noted the swing in selection criteria away from jet pilot time and toward higher levels of education, Aldrin, who held a doctor's degree from MIT, was the specific example always referred to — something he was not particularly fond of. But his nickname, Buzz, which erroneously suggested a "hot pilot" type, took some of the erudition out of his image. His manner was that of reserve without intellectual pretensions. When I first visited him in his Nassau Bay home in 1964, he struck me immediately as a man of considerable self-discipline and dignity. In appearance, he was of average height with a somewhat square face and firm jaw. His balding blond hair gave him a high forehead, but the most dominant thing about his face was his light blue eyes, which looked at you very directly and calmly.

His father, a retired Air Force colonel, who also had a doctorate from MIT, had settled in Montclair, New Jersey. Buzz, as he had been called since he was a baby, followed in his father's footsteps by attending West Point. He graduated third in his class of 475. Like Armstrong, he joined the Air Force and ended up in Korea where he shot down two MIG–15 jets. After Korea and his studies at MIT, where he specialized in the complex science of orbital mechanics, he decided he wanted to become an astronaut. His credentials, physical condition and reputation were excellent, and he was selected. When he flew four days in Gemini 12 with Jim Lovell, he saw practical application of many of the theoretical concepts he had first worked out at MIT.

His wife Joan, whom he had first met while he was at West Point, was an unusually accomplished woman. For a while, in fact, she was better known in the NASA–Clear Lake area than her husband. A group of people interested in the theater leased a former movie house in nearby League City, and Joan, it was quickly discovered, was an excellent and willing actress. I collected historical props for some of the plays and often admired her talent during rehearsals. Her husband joined the many fine ovations she received for her professional performances on the tiny stage in such plays as *Look Homeward, Angel* and *Playboy of the Western World*.

The appointment of Lieutenant Colonel Michael Collins to the highly coveted crew position in Apollo 11 was a widely applauded selection among NASA's engineers who had seen Collins perform at close range. Before the growth of a bone spur in his neck removed him from the Apollo 8 crew list, he had responded excellently to the year-long training in preparation for the first circumlunar mission. When he couldn't make it with Apollo 8 and was assigned instead as the prime ground voice communicator, his coolness and mastery of technical procedures was carefully noted by Deke Slayton and others at NASA. His Apollo 11 assignment was perhaps the toughest of all. As command module pilot he was to become the first man to circle the moon solo while his comrades went down to the surface in LEM.

The son of an Army general, Mike Collins was born in Rome while his father was military attaché to the American Embassy there. As an Army kid, he moved a great deal and picked up some facility in foreign languages both in the street and the private schools he attended. Predictably, he went to West Point where his academic record was not particularly outstanding. Upon graduation, the yearbook noted beside his name: "Stay casual . . . he took the cash and let the credit go . . ." Like Armstrong, he became a test pilot at Edwards where any disinclination to fly solo was overcome in a hurry.

He became a member of the "third class" of astronauts in 1963 and subsequently flew with John Young in Gemini 10, a rendezvous and space walk mission. During Collins's space walk, he successfully checked out the Zot gun that propelled him in space, Buck Rogers fashion. But when he reentered the craft, he accidentally left his camera and film outside, and somehow both the telephone-book-sized flight plan and the package for one of the scientific experiments vanished into space through the entry hatch.

From his appearance and manner, one would never guess that Mike Collins was the best handball player among the astronauts. He had bright, dark eyes, thin, very mobile lips, delicate features, a "high forehead," brown hair and an altogether noncombative type of personality. He was very respectful of the wishes and feelings of other people, most of whom refer to him as the epitome of a "nice guy." Since his school days, he had been fond of sleeping as much as he could, and he deliberately refused to fertilize his lawn so he wouldn't have to cut it often. He and his wife Pat had three children.

I had seen Neil and Buzz together three months earlier, in mid-April, when they simulated their lunar surface duties for the first time in their new pressure suits and heavy back packs. It was indoor simulation with LEM perched on a gravelly and sandy surface that had been spread out on the concrete floor of one of MSC's high bay buildings. As they practiced and exerted themselves against the stiff and girdling confinement of the blue-shoed pressure suits, both moved about with slowly deliberate, high-stepping, robot-like movements. Neil, especially, adopted a weird-looking stride that had the awkwardness of a man walking on stilts. From time to time they had to remove their helmets and sit down to rest. I remember Neil's flushed face, heavy panting and the way his blond hair had turned black from sweat and became plastered down around his forehead and temples. Yet each time the exhausting simulation was resumed, Neil stood up quickly and eagerly like a sweating boxer impatient for another round to begin.

On July 5, I had watched Neil, Buzz and Mike stride across the MSC stage wearing gas masks. Then they removed their masks and sat at three chairs in the mouth of a plastic tunnel through which air was forced toward the press audience by a huge turbine fan blowing from behind them. NASA was supersensitive now on the subject of illness in space, and this fan was NASA's elaborate precaution against any of the astronauts catching a virus just ten days before the scheduled flight.

Members of the press—most of whom felt such precautions were a form of "overkill" on NASA's part — had passed out dozens of surgical face masks as a joke. No one in the audience wore them, however, except the Japanese. No one had explained the joke to them, and Japanese photographers, cameramen and reporters very solemnly wore the masks throughout the briefing. The use of such precautions is quite common in Japan, where people with colds frequently wear face masks while walking and shopping.

Each astronaut in turn gave a highly technical briefing on planned flight events, explaining to us the code names *Eagle* and *Columbia* as well as their improvised plans for sleeping on the moon. The entire briefing had an unreal quality to it. Far from recognizing the historic significance of the proposed mission, the men who were to make it seemed to dodge and escape the historic implications through their wordy preoccupation with the technical ways and means of getting there. For the most part, they spoke in esoteric engineering terms often called NASA-ese.

Reporters, sensing that a sort of barrier of technological preoccupation existed between them and their subjects sitting beneath the American flag, tried to break through to the inner men.

James Gunn of the BBC asked, "What will your plans be in the extremely unlikely event that the lunar module does not come up from the surface?"

Neil gave his serious, slightly ironic smile.

"We've chosen not to think about that up to the present time. We don't think that's at all a likely situation; it's simply a possible one . . . At the present time we're left without recourse should that occur."

Asked later how he would spend the remaining time if they were marooned on the moon's surface, Aldrin drew a laugh by replying, "I'd probably spend it working on the availability of the ascent engine."

"Colonel Collins," someone asked at one point, "you would appear to have the most frustrating job on the mission, not going all the way. How do you feel about that?"

Collins answered immediately and firmly, "I don't feel in the slightest bit frustrated. I'm going ninety-nine and nine-tenths percent of the way there, and that suits me just fine."

There was not much applause at the end of the astronauts' last press conference before liftoff. I had the feeling that questions, especially personal questions were considered irrelevant by the astronauts. The space program needed selling, yes, and they were willing to do it—but I felt that they wanted to pick a better time than during their final phase training. There were still so many things to learn and practice, so many fine points to hone. Why waste words talking about irrelevancies?

Early on the clear morning of July 15, Armstrong, Aldrin and Collins were gently awakened for the start of the Apollo 11 mission. Shortly afterwards, I got out of my bed in the back of my rental car and was surprised to see that during the night, the entire open field had filled with automobiles. In the damp, pre-dawn darkness, traffic was already moving north in the direction of the launch complex. At one of the press buses, I finally found an old friend, B. G. MacNabb, at whose home Walter Cronkite and I had sometimes stayed during early Mercury and Gemini flights. Mister Mac — or as he was once known, Mister Atlas — had been in charge of getting the early Atlas rockets ready for flight at a time when Atlas was the mightiest rocket in the entire Free World. Now, he seemed as confused as I was by all the unfamiliar faces of the spectator press. There was a time when Mister Mac and I knew everyone on the press buses by their first names. But time and the transcendent mission of Apollo 11 had flooded out and dispersed the original and once jovial fraternity of knowledgeable rocketeers. We were surrounded by enthusiastic amateurs who were thrilled at their first pre-dawn convergence at Land's End. They shoved and jostled for a seat on the bus like a holiday crowd going to the horse tracks.

We moved north through double lines of traffic that crept between ranks of parked cars. On gravel shoulders and grass-flanked causeways, a generation of Americans had come to witness the moon shot like the Scandinavians who had once come to an icy fjord to see the departure of a Viking long ship on a sea-girdling mission which for its time was no less of an adventure than this launch.

At the main gate, guards waved us on automatically. Back in the 1950s when our rocket arsenal was a high-security military base, how I had longed to go through these gates! I had finally become the first journalist to do so only after signing a statement that I would report nothing of what I saw inside. I first went in not as a journalist but as a movie director to photograph the first scenes ever taken inside a blockhouse for a secret Air Force film. Of course, everything I saw and heard then was burned into my memory, and I later wrote it all up for *Time* magazine as soon as I heard the Washington press corps was to be flown down to the Cape for the first press tour. When members of the press checked into their motels I had had extra copies of fresh *Time* magazines placed in the lobby. Across the cover, a yellow banner read, *Inside the Gates at Cape Canaveral*. The first map of the Cape area appeared inside, a map formerly so secret that for months I had kept its hand-drawn predecessor inside a big red envelope in the back of my clothes closet.

"How in the hell did they get here first?" I heard one Washington journalist mutter. It was the first and cleanest scoop I ever had.

As the bus crept along in the bumper-to-bumper traffic towards the press complex, some literary history came to mind. It was almost exactly a century ago that science-fiction writer Jules Verne envisioned a spaceship that would take off for flight to the moon. By an astonishing coincidence, Verne had located his fictional launch pad in Florida. Verne's science-trained brother often advised him and must have known that the further south you go toward the equator, the more initial velocity is given a rocket by the spinning motion of the earth.

Judging by the crowds assembled at the press site, Verne had also correctly foreseen the public impact of a flight to the moon. The huge grandstand was already more than half filled. Behind it were rows of outdoor toilets and about fifty aluminum and white press trailers with dusty, serpentine cables coiled among them. Several hundred camera tripods were lined up at the edge of a small tidal lagoon between us and the now compellingly visible target, giant pad 39A on which the world's greatest astrovehicle thirty-six stories tall waited. The most vital property at the press center was a telephone, and long rows of them had been claimed, staked out, labeled, first-come-first-served, and were now guarded with that particularly virulent proprietariness with which newsmen protect their one link to the waiting world. Without a mouthpiece, a newsman may as well be at home in bed, and woe unto any other man who touches his sacred instrument.

A Spanish reporter shouted into his phone, trying to make himself understood in Madrid. Bob Considine, whose typewriter for decades had tapped out stories for Hearst, now had a telephone. William F. Buckley, conservative publisher of *National Review*, had no phone because he had no urgent deadline. Blind commentator Brian Wallach of radio station WFAS in White Plains, New York, held onto a German shepherd dog named Fax. Pulitzer Prize-writer Norman Mailer, wearing Hush Puppies, had to stand in line for over forty minutes to get a single cup of coffee from a broken vending machine. Dame Sybil Leek of the *Ladies' Home Journal* meant to attract, and attracted, attention in her flowing purple muumuu. Cronkite, Brinkley and Bergman were already on the air from their network trailers.

I spoke briefly with the distinguished British space writer and father of the communication satellite Arthur C. Clarke, who, as the sun came up, was taking his own pictures with an inexpensive camera. He had long ago predicted and written about flights to the moon, but on this morning he seemed most excited about the fact that his movie *2001—A Space Odyssey* was being shown at that very moment at the Moscow Film Festival. When I had last talked to him he had just returned from the filming sessions and — unlike most authors — had been pleased with the way it was going.

The sun came higher and brighter, and by 9 A.M. Bob Considine was already sweating through his gray plaid sports coat. The countdown was on schedule; it was thirty-two minutes to launch.

For a while I walked away from the crowded press area to the edge of a hammock of oily green palmetto palms. I knew the contents of the hammock and the nearby tidal lagoon well, having often fished from the Cape Canaveral beaches long before the area became a space center. I had often tramped through the lush palm hammocks where as late as 1956 a family of Florida panthers had lived. Once on a fishing trip, I saw one of the sleek animals lope across the sandy rut road in front of my car. With the naturalist Roger Tory Peterson, Farida Wiley of New York's Museum of Natural History and official Audubon Society photographer Allan Cruickshank, I had searched out rare birds in this area during several of the annual Audubon bird counts. It occurred to me that this particular patch of Land's End symbolized, contained and told much about life on mother-planet earth. It was a stark contrast to the new land Armstrong, Aldrin and Collins were heading for. Just a few hundred yards from pad 39A were the warm lands that have sustained life on earth for millions of years. Nearby were seas teeming with fish, shrimp and plankton; placid lagoons ringed with eelgrass, rushes and thistle; subtropical forests containing curious raccoons, shy swamp hares, primitive armadillos and some of the oldest reptiles on earth: alligators, horned lizards, rattlesnakes, chameleons and tortoises. Within thirty miles of the rocket's base, there were more varieties of birds than in any comparable area in the continental United States — from purple gallinules which walk on lily pads to rare pine siskins. And within this ecological Eden, man had erected a tall, white astrovehicle that Dr. Robert H. Goddard decades ago had called a "rocket train."

On this day, the train with its three astroconductors would leave the fertile, hospitable earth and plunge toward a barren, forbidding moon — a hot-cold desert moon hostile to life.

The moon called to man. It called him to an elliptical-shaped, crater-pocked flatland known by the code name Sasser. Alien, airless, austere, lifeless, stark, dry, Sasser had not changed its expression for 3.5 billion years. Located in the immense Sea of Tranquility, Sasser was both lure and threshold. This was where man was scheduled to leave footprints that could last for thousands of years. This was where astronauts would pick up bits and pieces of pay dirt, priceless fragments of the hoary old face of timeless Sasser.

This then was the target and destination. The journey to it could be both a door to the future and a window to the past.

The journey began at 9:32 on the morning of July 16. By then, I had moved back among the professional witnesses. An IBM friend had already told me that in the intricate planning for the flight his computers had to take into account the fact that without being launched the command and service module already had traveled 436 feet above earth's sea level on its journey to the moon. It had gotten that far just in being hoisted to the top of the Saturn rocket. Now in a miracle moment engineers call "first motion," the CSM rose to 437 feet. Pushing it up and through the 437-foot mark in awesome silence was a great, two-pronged, rusty orange column of smoke and white-hot jets of flame that billowed out over Land's End. Five white ibises that were winging toward the rocket appeared to stop in midair, fell off, then, black-tipped wings pumping furiously, they wheeled and headed in the opposite direction.

The rocket cleared the tower. Cheers erupted. Shouts. Tears on young and old faces. Heart rates were dispassionately recorded: Armstrong, 110 beats per minute (down 36 beats from his first flight in Gemini); Collins, 99 (down 26); and Buzz Aldrin, an implacable 88 (down 22).

Now came the out-of-phase sound of ignition, late and thunderous. Its surging detonation built rapidly to a roar that resonated in my lung cavities, sinuses, bone marrow. The rocket pierced and blew a clean round hole in a gauzy sheet of low level scud and then its stiletto shadow raced away across the top of the translucent cloud to-

ward the northwest. The continuous reverberating detonation of the climbing rocket was almost overpowering.

If it's only been seen and heard on a television set, it's
never really been seen and heard.

Norman Mailer, the best journalist there — or maybe
anywhere — who was watching and feeling his first
rocket launch, later wrote that the sound he heard came
"like the crackling of wood twigs over the ridge, came
with the sharp and furious bark of a million drops of oil
crackling suddenly into combustion . . . Then came
the ear splitting bark of a thousand machine guns firing
at once . . . the thunderous murmur of Niagaras of
flame roaring conceivably louder than the loudest thun-
ders . . . and the earth began to shake and would not
stop."

A few minutes later, Neil said calmly, "In-board cutoff," and what Mailer called "a ship of flames" was on its
way to the moon. When I had seen the launch of Explorer 1, our first satellite, I had felt its authority so
strongly that the flight seemed utterly irrevocable. There
could be no abort — no turning back. Now this flight
had it. I knew it was not going to stop.

Later I saw Jo Farren, a bright girl who had been head
researcher on a book on space I wrote for the National
Geographic Society. I had told her before the flight that
she would cry.

"Did you cry?" I asked her after the excited crowd
murmurs at the press site settled down.

"Yes," she said with fierce pride, "I cried."

At the instant the Saturn rocket cleared the pad 39A
tower, control of the mission was passed to the Manned

Spacecraft Center in Houston. When the press bus finally broke through the traffic jams outside the gates, I bought an armload of newspaper extras and caught the first plane back to Houston to cover the rest of the mission at the elaborately prepared MSC press center.

We had learned from Sir Bernard Lovell, the garrulous "sage" of the Jodrell Bank tracking station in Cheshire, England, that, inexplicably, a Soviet spacecraft called Luna 15 was also on its way to the moon. Commented correspondent Buddy Martin of the Cape Kennedy newspaper *Today*, "No, there is no race between the United States and Russia. There is no race in the American and National League baseball teams either. And God didn't make little green apples."

All preliminary Apollo 11 flight events, so well rehearsed in precursor flights, went well — earth orbit injection, translunar injection, the turnaround and docking with LEM, and the long coasting flight. Then, on July 19, Apollo 11 prepared for LOI, lunar orbit insertion.

"Eleven, this is Houston. You are go for LOI. Over."

"Roger, go for LOI."

"And we've had loss of signal as Apollo 11 goes behind the moon."

There were no dramatics as the terse and all-business crew of Apollo 11 emerged from its first transit behind the moon and flashed pictures of the moon on television.

"It was like perfect," Buzz commented.

"This view is worth the price of the trip," Neil said.

The next day, July 20, was scheduled to mark the beginning of a new era. Mike Collins alone in the command module *Columbia* watched carefully as Armstrong and Aldrin undocked *Eagle*. *Eagle* rotated slowly as Collins inspected it.

"How does it look?" Armstrong asked.

"The *Eagle* has wings," Collins replied.

Half an orbit later, *Eagle* had separated far enough to begin DOI, descent orbit insertion.

"Listen, babe," Collins said to ground communicator Charlie Duke, "everything is going just swimmingly, beautiful."

If crew members felt any apprehension over the mysterious Russian spaceship Luna 15, also now in lunar orbit, they concealed it well. The Russians had made no detailed announcement. Frank Borman's initiative in telephoning a leading Soviet scientist relieved some — but not all — of the suspense when he received assurance that Luna 15 would not interfere with the flight of Apollo 11. The lack of known intentions, as much as the presence of a possibly competitive lunar landing, heightened the suspense as the most critical and untested maneuver of the entire Apollo flight began.

Armstrong had already commented on the jumbled blocks of materials in some of the craters, and now quite unexpectedly he was to get a frightening close-up view of these landing obstacles. Like hundreds of other newsmen, including 117 from Japan, I was waiting in MSC's huge auditorium where NASA, with typical redundancy, had rigged two giant TV screens on the stage.

After the DOI burn, *Eagle* swung around behind the moon approaching the precise position where the final descent burn would begin to take the men down toward the surface. As final descent began, Mission Control radioed *Eagle,* "Everything is looking good here."

"Looks real good," *Eagle* replied. "Our position check appears to be a little long . . . We've got data dropout."

The big descent engine was now burning, slowing and lowering *Eagle.* At 21,000 feet, the descent speed had been reduced to 1,210 feet per second. At 4,200 feet above the moon, Mission Control said simply, "You're go."

Then came the final seconds before the dangerous and unrehearsable touchdown. Neil's pulse rate climbed rapidly toward its peak of 156 beats per minute.

*Eagle:* "Lights on. Down two and a half. Forward. Forward. Good. Forty feet. Down two and a half. Picking up some dust. Thirty feet. Two and a half down. Faint shadow. Four forward. Drifting to the right a little. Contact light. Okay, engine stop."

The silence was uncertain and profound. Was *Eagle* upright? Were they actually on the surface? No one yet knew whether or not to cheer.

Suddenly, Neil's voice came on loud and a bit shaken, perhaps by radio static.

"Tranquility Base here. The *Eagle* has landed."

Replied Mission Control: "Tranquility, we copy you on the ground. You got a bunch of guys that's about to turn blue. We're breathing again. Thanks a lot."

All bedlam broke loose at the press center. Some newsmen raced for phones. Others kept tapes or notes going. My movie-director friend Don Wiseman grinned and lit the cigar he had been rolling in his fingers. The cheering could be stopped by only one thing: the sound of additional comment from the moon's surface.

Said Neil, "The auto targeting was taking us right into a football field-sized crater, with a large number of big boulders and rocks about one or two crater diameters around us, and it required flying manually over the rock field to find a reasonably good area."

The automatic system had been designed for just such a contingency takeover by the pilot. Neil had overridden the automatic controls about two minutes before touchdown when he first saw the formidable rock field.

Now Buzz came on with his first view:

"We'll get to the details of what's around here, but it looks like a collection of just about every variety of shapes, angularities, granularities, every variety of rock you could find. The colors vary pretty much depending on how you're looking relative to the zero phase point [of sunlight]. There doesn't appear to be too much of a general color at all. However, it looks as though some of the rocks and boulders, of which there are quite a few in the near area, are going to have some interesting colors in them."

Neil reported he had no difficulty at all with one-sixth G, "At least, it's immediately natural to move in this environment."

Mission Control suddenly remembered Mike Collins, in *Columbia*, orbiting the moon entirely alone.

GROUND TO *Columbia*: *Eagle* is at Tranquility. Over.
*Columbia*: Yeah, I heard the whole thing.

GROUND: Tranquility. Be advised that there's a lot of smiling faces in this room and all over the world. Over.

TRANQUILITY: There's two of them up here.

GROUND: It was a beautiful job, you guys.

*Columbia:* And don't forget me in the command module . . . It sure sounded great from up here. You guys did a fantastic job.

TRANQUILITY: Thank you, Neil said. Just keep that orbiting base ready for us up there now.

Neil had already reported that they "hadn't picked things out on the horizon yet," meaning that they didn't know exactly where they were.

The ground replied, "Roger, Tranquility, we'll figure it out." But it was easier said than done. Everyone involved was aware that knowledge of *Eagle*'s exact location was essential to the vital ascent and rendezvous maneuvers because of fuel limitations. The public was not aware of it at the time, but while the entire world rejoiced at a successful landing and *Eagle*'s crew went through their long checklists preparatory to walking on the surface, the problem of *Eagle*'s location on the surface was causing furrowed brows and deep concern in inner NASA and contractor circles. While the press was generally reporting a highly dramatic success story, I left the MSC auditorium and met privately with some of the men who early recognized the seriousness of the location problem. When Mike Collins orbiting overhead repeatedly was unable to sight any reflections off *Eagle*, or other indications of the landing location, these men became so concerned that they had to forego their roles as absorbed spectators and neglect all other problems except this one.

It was in these private offices that I learned the seriousness of the "data dropouts" that had occurred during descent. The computers knew *Eagle*'s position before descent. If descent data had been continuous, the computers would have quickly pinpointed the surface location. It then would have been a simple matter for the high-speed computers to calculate the exact ascent burn and trajectory required to link up again with *Columbia* without exhausting fuel supplies. The problem was that neither the computers nor their human masters knew where *Eagle* was located on the surface of the moon. Nothing Neil and Buzz could see provided a usable clue.

As I went back to watch the lunar walk and surface activity on NASA's television, I knew there was one piece of information that NASA was not yet ready to relay to the moon: that the data dropouts and Collins's inability to pinpoint visually where the *Eagle* was meant that Charlie Duke's confident "We'll figure it out" might prove extremely difficult to follow through on. Cancellation of the surface activity was not considered because flight planners needed all possible time to work out the problem.

NASA's great stage screens were blank with expectant darkness, but we could hear the broadcast lunar voices as clearly as if *Eagle* itself were on the stage instead of a quarter of a million miles away.

GROUND: Do you think you can open the hatch at this pressure of about point one, two psi?

NEIL: We're going to try it.
GROUND: Roger.
NEIL: The hatch is coming open.

Guided by Buzz Aldrin, Neil Armstrong in his bulky suit and back pack worked his way through the *Eagle*'s forward hatch like a chick emerging from its eggshell.

NEIL: How am I doing?
BUZZ: You're doing fine.
NEIL: Okay, Houston, I'm on the porch.
BUZZ: Roger, Neil.

The tension was broken in the MSC auditorium as an abstract black and white picture came on both the huge screens. Then, suddenly, we could make out Neil's ghostly image on the ladder.

"I'm at the foot of the ladder," he announced clearly. "The LM footpads are only depressed in the surface about one or two inches . . . I'm going to step off the LM now."

We saw his left foot exploring down, touching, withdrawing, then stepping full weight, joined by the right.

"That's one small step for man. One giant leap for mankind," he announced from the surface of the moon.

Again cheers. Again an incredible sense of astonishment that millions on earth could actually see him emerge from man's twenty million years in the incubator of the earth's benign atmosphere. He stood now firmly on timeless Sasser.

"There seems to be no difficulty in moving around as we suspected . . . It's simply no trouble to walk around."

Neil, like a being newly born, ventured further away from his fractured egg.

"It has a stark beauty all its own," he commented. "It's like much of the high desert of the United States. It's different but it's very pretty out here . . . The surface is fine and powdery. I can pick it up loosely with my toe. It does adhere in fine layers like powdered charcoal to the sole and sides of my boots . . . I only go in, oh a fraction of an inch. Maybe an eighth of an inch. But I can see the footprints of my boots and the treads in the fine sandy particles."

Those of us on earth now could see them too. Now it was Buzz Aldrin's turn. "Is it okay for me to come out?" he asked. He was already on the ladder, a second ghost barely distinguishable from the first.

BUZZ: Are you ready?
NEIL: All set.
BUZZ: Now I want to back up and partially close the hatch. Making sure not to lock it on my way out.
NEIL (laughing): Particularly good thought.
BUZZ: That's our home for the next couple of hours and I want to take good care of it.

Buzz stepped down, then cautiously leapt back up to be sure he could again reach the lower ring. Then holding himself by his hands, he jumped down again with both feet.

BUZZ: That's a good step.
NEIL: Yep, about a three-footer.
BUZZ: Beautiful, beautiful.

NEIL: Isn't that something. Magnificent sight down here . . . Isn't it fun?

Buzz Aldrin obviously agreed, but first came some formalism, a little ritual.

In front of the television camera, Neil read from the plaque attached to the side of *Eagle: Here men from the Planet Earth first set foot upon the Moon, July 1969* A.D. *We came in peace for all mankind.*

The plaque was signed by all three crew members and the President of the United States.

Now it was Buzz Aldrin's turn to have a little fun that was, nevertheless, in the interest of science. Completely disregarding the fact that a broken leg could mean death on the moon, he began to run, jump and hop about the moon's surface. Half floating at times like a marionette on a string, he scattered fine-grained lunar debris as each step squirted bits of soil that arced back like no fountain droplets on earth. The soil particles seemed to spring out like lazy unmagnetized fragments which splashed back to the surface stickily like wet sand. Time seemed suspended, and motion seemed mesmerized and languorously distorted. He talked, partly panting, as he drifted through his weird-gaited choreography on the lesser gravity of the spongy and unfamiliar lunar stage. At times his body, carrying 183 extra pounds of earth weight, tilted eerily to one side while one or both feet were off the ground.

"All right," Aldrin relayed, "you do have to be rather careful to keep track of where your center of mass is. Sometimes, it takes about two or three paces to make sure that you've got your feet underneath you. About two or three or maybe four easy paces can bring you to a nearly smooth stop. Like a football player, you just have to split out to the side and cut a little bit . . . One called a kangeroo hop does work, but it seems that your forward ability is not quite as good."

Neil moved the camera to a new position. Later, the two sank the shaft of a United States flag with some difficulty into the unexpected hardness of the subsurface soil. The flag, stiffened with wire, appeared to be suspended in a rigid horizontal in the airless void.

"Neil and Buzz," Mission Control suddenly interrupted, "the President of the United States is in his office now and would like to say a few words to you. Over."

NEIL: That would be an honor.

MISSION CONTROL: Go ahead, Mr. President. This is Houston. Out.

PRESIDENT NIXON: Hello, Neil and Buzz. I am talking to you by telephone from the Oval Room at the White House. And this certainly has to be the most historic telephone call ever made. Because of what you have done, the heavens have become a part of man's world. And as you talk to us from the Sea of Tranquility, it inspires us to redouble our efforts to bring peace and tranquility to earth. For one priceless moment, in the whole history of man, all the people on this earth are truly one. One in their pride in what you have done. And one in our prayers, that you will return safely to earth.

The speech seemed strangely stilted, as incongruous as a commercial in the middle of a love scene. Neil replied almost in kind. "Thank you, Mr. President. It's a great honor and privilege for us to be here representing not only the United States but men of peace of all nations, and with interest and a curiosity and a vision for the future. It's an honor for us to be able to participate here today."

Sense of wonder maligned, there was work to do and precious little time in which to do it. The two ghosts set about prospecting and collecting rocks, setting up lunar surface experiments, taking lunar core samples, traversing back and forth and occasionally running. Silent at times, the automatons sometimes panted or came alive in the familiar audio of worldly persiflage. On the television screen it was impossible at times to tell one from another.

Struggling with the leveling device on one of the surface packages, Buzz said at one point, "Would you believe the ball is right in the middle now."

"Wonderful," said Neil. "Take a picture before it moves."

Hauling up the precious rock boxes with a rope hoist to Buzz on the porch, the Neil robot said, "If you can kinda hold her, I think I can do the pulling."

They rechecked the two surface devices they would leave on the moon: a seismometer to radio to earth the severity of possible lunar quakes or meteor impacts, and a reflector designed to bounce a laser beam from earth back to its source so the moon's precise distance could be measured by timing the interval between sending and receiving the laser signal.

As the allotted moon time rapidly drew to a close, both of the men had to rush to load the last of the ap-

*Armstrong and Aldrin prospecting on the lunar surface*

proximately sixty pounds (earth weight) of rocks and soil they were to bring back. Time did not permit the planned survey and mapping of the rock locations.

Finally, like a parent or teacher, earth, redundant even with words, interrupted recess.

"Buzz, this is Houston. You have approximately three minutes until you must commence EVA termination activities. Over."

"Roger. Understand," said the obedient children of Selene. The experience in an alien world of a far and ancient land, of scientific work that was like human child's play, of preoccupation tasks at the expense of a long, wondering, absorbing, childlike gaze around, was nearly at an end.

"Head on up the ladder," the parent-teacher urged,

and the ghostly marionettes, drawn by invisible strings from earth, were pulled back in, and the shell closed around them. It had been the fastest two hours, thirteen minutes and twelve seconds, from first step to last, on earth or the moon.

While the new and exhausted scholars of Selene slept cramped like crumpled costumes against the hard metal panels inside the shell, LEM stood, slightly askew, before the remote TV camera, a patient, dutiful moon bug. And a quarter of a million miles away other men still wrestled with their key location problem. They were close to the time when they had to make a decision.

The question was: were they here? Or there? There was no way to explain the problem except in the esoteric language of NASA-ese: optics from the CSM, one of them said, had failed. "What we need next time is a parabolic reflector on LM that will gain the attention of CSM, give a brief reflection, at least, like a curved windshield." Computers of PNGS (Primary Navigation Guidance System) and AGS (Abort Guidance System) together said they were at lunar coordinates .799N and 23.4602E, exactly 937.501 miles from the center of the moon mass. But the rendezvous radar solution, derived from the known orbit of CSM and the angular position of LM with respect to the known orbit, said they were at .7422N and 23.4849E and 937.131 miles from the center of moon mass. Sextant sightings on the sun and on known positions on earth, although they were considered, would be too complicated and possibly unreliable. They were not exactly lost, but which was right — PNGS-AGS or rendezvous radar?

"When PNGS and AGS give nearly agreeing solutions," one man said to me privately, "there is little doubt but that an average solution between the two is close. We would like to have had an MSFN (Manned Space Flight Radar Data) solution as well, and a certain worth could have come from Collins, if he could just see the base. But we'll have to take an average with rendezvous radar and feed that position to the on-board computers. It's a calculated risk, and let's hope the fuel holds."

When a tiny pinpoint dot was placed on a fresh lunar chart, the whole complex mechanism of the first surface to lunar-orbit rendezvous depended on its accuracy. So absorbing was this delicate maneuver that there was time only to barely acknowledge the news that Luna 15, its mission still unknown, had crashed five hundred miles away in — semantically appropriately — the Sea of Crises.

On Monday morning, July 21, as I watched Van Heflin on NBC, I heard space poetry in one ear and the ascent engine countdown in the other. *Eagle*'s crew had already tossed out garbage, junk and even excess Hasselblad cameras whose lunar impact was recorded on earth from the nearby passive seismic indicator. They had spent just over twenty-one hours on the moon.

Finally, the ground said, "Our guidance recommendation is PNGS and you're cleared for takeoff."

"Roger," *Eagle* replied, "Understand. We're number one on the runway." Neil's heart rate climbed to 90; Buzz's to 120.

At 12:55, the upper half of *Eagle* ignited as its thrust forced the saucer-shaped footpads of *Eagle*'s descent engine section — now a launch platform — further into the surface of the moon. For the second time there was fire on the moon. They lifted, riding on an aurora of flame.

"That was beautiful," *Eagle* said. "We're going right down U.S. One."

Up *Eagle* rose over the now familiar harshly pitted face of the moon. The ascent engine cut off at 60,000 feet. If it had burned true, the astronauts would coast into a lunar orbit that would permit rendezvous with the command module. Later, in *Columbia*, Mike Collins confirmed radar reports that the Tranquility Base location and burn calculations had been the correct ones. He recognized *Eagle*'s approaching flashing beacon with a rise in heart rate. On *Columbia*'s twenty-eighth orbit, the two craft were reunited. About an hour later, after Neil and Buzz had transferred themselves and their heavy vacuum-sealed rock boxes inside *Columbia*, the ascent stage of *Eagle* — its mission fully and victoriously accounted for — was cast loose.

It was time for the final burn in lunar orbit, TEI or transearth injection. Again and for the last time they went behind the moon. Again we waited. At acquisition of signal, Charlie Duke said, "Hello, Apollo 11, Houston. How did it go? Over."

"Time to open up the LRL [Lunar Receiving Laboratory] doors, Charlie."

"Roger. We got you coming home."

The crew now rested. "There's nothing but static and silence coming from Apollo 11," Mission Control reported a few hours later.

For the first time, earthmen could relax and try to understand the incomprehensible. Plaudits, congratulations, superlatives poured in from all over the globe. In Paris, Frenchmen could remember nothing on American television — with the possible exception of the assassination of President Kennedy — that had commanded so much attention there. President Nixon called it "a moment of transcendent drama." The entire world had obviously been caught up in the astonishing extraterrestrial adventure.

When the crew awoke, there came from Apollo 11 curious sounds of revelry and merriment. Jim Maloney, listening on the ground, said it sounded like "a ball-sized New Year's Eve party."

"Are you sure," Charlie Duke asked the happy crew, "that you don't have anyone in there with you?"

"Where," Mike Collins asked, "does the White Team go during off-hours?" Fun and games in cislunar space. The White Team was one of the three round-the-clock shifts in Mission Control.

On the ground, great chunks and pages and spools and computer printouts and displays of the mission of Apollo 11 had been recorded for a later time, but tracking and positioning data were still crucial to terminal entry and splashdown. There was no celebration yet in Mission Control. The unwritten law was "hold the cigars and corks until they're standing on the carrier deck."

Because of a massive Pacific thunderstorm, the landing area had to be shifted 250 miles, a contingency now handled in quite a routine manner. At 11:25 on the morning of July 24, Apollo 11 was barreling right down the middle of the new corridor. Seven minutes later entry began at 400,000 feet. First visual contact: 11:39. First visual sighting from the carrier; *Hornet:* 11:42.

"Come on, Houston," pleaded Walter Cronkite. "Give us the word."

Chutes sighted: 11:52. The flight plan called for splashdown at 195 hours, 19 minutes and 5 seconds into the mission; it came at 195 hours, 18 minutes and 21 seconds — 44 highly permissible seconds early. By 12:57, Neil, Buzz and Mike were on the carrier deck where the President waited. Corks popped everywhere. The rest was instant replay and video tapes vaulted for eternity, flags, cigars, speeches, jokes, reunion and relief.

To avoid possible lunar contamination everything the three touched on earth, including life rafts, was thoroughly disinfected. The three men, wearing biological isolation garments, immediately entered their trailer to begin their long isolation. They and their lunar nuggets were to be taken directly to Houston, to enter an elaborately and expensively prepared $8 million facility for the period of quarantine.

Before the flight, I had asked Dr. Persa Raymond Bell, chief of MSC's Lunar and Earth Sciences Division and director of the Lunar Receiving Laboratory, to show me through his three-story, $8.5 million facility.

"We don't really expect to find dangerous organisms in the lunar samples," Dr. Bell told me, "but you must remember this port of entry has responsibility for the entire planet. We can't be too careful."

The lunar astronauts greeted their families through the glass window of their quarantine trailer when it landed at

*Armstrong, Collins and Aldrin*

nearby Ellington Air Force Base. Then they were trucked to the guarded portals of Dr. Bell's unique laboratory. Once inside, they were greeted by the team of doctors, psychologists and technicians who were to live with them in quarantine. Their quarters were modern and spacious. An operating room had even been provided for a possible emergency.

Some of the precious rocks went underground to a spotless silver and white room where a thoroughly tested radiation counter was isolated. The counter sat like a squat, stolid furnace inside a labyrinthine entrance tunnel that eliminated cosmic rays which travel only in straight lines. Here beneath the ground the radiation count was designed to show only ray emissions from the lunar samples.

Elsewhere in the huge lab, over a hundred specially selected biologists, chemists and electron microscopy experts went to work sterilizing, weighing, cutting, grinding, sorting and analyzing the rocks and soil samples. Using remote-controlled equipment to avoid possible contamination, they quickly established the lack of any known or unknown germs, or biological specimens, in either astronauts or surface samples. The startling things they did discover are detailed in a later chapter.

To many, the elaborate quarantine precautions seemed entirely unnecessary, but it was not until Sunday night, August 11 — twenty-five days after the historic journey began — that Dr. Charles Berry broke the seal on the medical prison. The Communicable Disease Center in Atlanta had finally cleared the astronauts' blood samples. All three crewmen looked weary and pale as they emerged into the public spotlight and flashbulbs.

Armstrong made a brief speech in front of the microphones. "I can't say that I would choose to spend a couple of weeks like that, but I am glad we had the opportunity to complete the mission."

Then they were free to walk quickly under a moonless sky to their waiting families.

The rocks would be examined and reexamined for decades, but for the crew which had brought them from the timeless surface of the Sea of Tranquility the mission of Apollo 11 was over. The three scholars of Selene had come home. It now remained only for man to judge whether their remarkable space odyssey was a culmination, or a beginning.

# 11

# Apollo 12—
# the Lunar Bull's-eye

*The name of the game in Apollo 12 is lunar surface exploration.*

— ASTRONAUT CHARLES "PETE" CONRAD

UNLIKE ALL PREVIOUS manned space flights, the scientific and human suspense of Apollo 11 did not end when the astronauts were safely reunited with their families. The reason, of course, was the presence of some sixty pounds of lunar rock samples which under almost daily intensive examination gave, or promised to give, new surprises. After several weeks of examination, however, it began to be clear to the insistent press and hopeful public that no sudden, dramatic solution to the moon's origin in space and time was likely to be forthcoming. As I waited in Houston for each new finding or talked privately to some of the scientists actually doing the investigation, I recalled a prophetic statement Dr. Eugene Shoemaker had once made. In 1968, I had flown to Flagstaff, Arizona, to spend two days with Dr. Shoemaker at his unique astrogeological laboratory located among Arizona's ponderosa pines.

"Unfortunately," Shoemaker had remarked at the time, "many people have the idea that once we land an astronaut on the moon and return him to earth with his rock samples, we can suddenly come to firm conclusions about the moon's origin and history. This is simply not so. For one thing, determining the moon's origin may require us to search out the oldest rocks on the moon, and this will take time."

Since Apollo 11 had proven the basic reliability of the Apollo hardware, the most important aspect of the Apollo 12 mission was, in effect, to prove Shoemaker's remark. Apollo 12 would land on a different place on the moon, and, at the urging of Shoemaker and a number of other scientific investigators, the Apollo 12 astronauts would survey much more carefully the precise location of each rock sample of the ninety to one hundred pounds of lunar payload collected for the return trip. This would help scientists to determine what characteristics of a lunar rock may have been due to the angle at which it rested on the surface. The rock's relation to incoming rays from the sun was of particular interest to scientists. To better enable the astronauts to do the required geologic survey work, their time on the moon was to be over twice that allowed for Apollo 11, with a rest period scheduled halfway through the lunar surface activities.

The selected landing site was the precise area in the Ocean of Storms where the six-hundred-pound Surveyor 3 lunar probe had landed in April 1967. Surveyor 3 had landed in an unnamed crater about fifty feet deep and six hundred feet across. This was a target incredibly difficult to pinpoint. Crew members themselves estimated they had only a fifty-fifty chance of landing close enough to Surveyor to walk to it. If possible, crew members were to examine Surveyor 3 for whatever evidence it could provide of conditions on the moon's surface — especially any change these conditions could cause in earth metals.

Selected to command Apollo 12 was one of the most individualistic of NASA's roster of over fifty astronauts. While most astronauts tend to merge into the unemotional, engineer-oriented, inarticulate and largely interchangeable astronaut stereotype, Charles "Pete" Conrad was very much his own man. For sheer exuberance, the short, irrepressible Princeton graduate with the conspicuous gap between two of his prominent front teeth had no match. At one private dinner party, I saw him get so carried away with a story he was telling that he laid down his knife and fork and actually got to his feet to finish his account with facial expressions and flamboyant gestures. When his story was done, the entire table erupted into laughter. He was full of energy, loud, often funny, outspoken, and seemed happiest when wearing outlandish and highly individualistic clothes.

One Sunday afternoon at a small flying field not far from the Manned Spacecraft Center, he showed up for a session of sailplane flying wearing an Australian digger hat with upturned side brim, a decorated and tasseled leather vest and old-fashioned soft leather leggings. He looked like an amiable clown and, as always, exuded a high sense of enjoyment. At first, while Pete flew the tow plane, a friend, Scott Royce, and I flew behind in the two-place sailplane. At about 3,500 feet altitude, Scott would cut us loose from Pete's tow plane and we would soar around awhile on our way back to earth.

Once when I flew with Pete in the tow plane, we suddenly let down into a beehive of airport activity. Small planes seemed to be coming at us from all directions. Pete knocked his outlandish hat back on his head, rammed the throttle forward and pulled the nose up to gain altitude.

"I'll take space any day," he grinned. "This flying stuff is really dangerous."

But for all his clowning and elaborate put-ons, when the chips were down, Pete Conrad's superb judgment and ability as a pilot were as solid as any man's. The tow plane he was flying was a beefed-up acrobatic model, and, when he showed me how it performed, I knew he was the sort of pilot you could trust absolutely even when upside down, or fishtailing and sideslipping in barely above the treetops. Despite his five-foot, six-inch height and 138-pound weight, he carried the authority of a master pilot who created and adhered to his own life style.

As a high school student, Conrad had performed dismally because of lack of interest in his books which were in a losing conflict with his interest in motorcycles. He joined the Navy, and the armed services sent him to Princeton, where he bought part interest in a light plane. He made the girl he then dated, Jane Dubose of nearby Bryn Mawr, pay her own part of the plane's gas bill. They are now married and have four rambunctious boys: Thomas, Christopher, Andrew and Peter.

One of those named to fly with Conrad, Richard F.

Gordon, had flown with Pete on Gemini, and, before that, in the Pacific where they were both fighter pilots. In fact, in their Navy days the two men had often joked about someday going to the moon together. Now they were to get their chance. Gordon — who was to assume Mike Collins's role as the pilot of the CSM, code-named *Yankee Clipper*—was originally from Seattle and majored in math at the University of Washington. As a Navy pilot, he won the Bendix Trophy in 1961 in a cross-country flight of two hours and forty-five minutes during which he set a new speed record of 870 miles per hour. His hobbies at one time were cooking and growing roses, but gourmet cooking turned out to be rather exotic for the six Gordon children. Dick and his wife Barbara were one of the few astronaut families who spent a great deal of attention and money on the interior decoration of their home.

Alan LeVern Bean of Wheeler and Fort Worth, Texas, was assigned to Buzz Aldrin's former position in LEM, which also was given a naval code name, *Intrepid*. Bean, at thirty-six, was the last of his class of astronauts to be given a space flight assignment. Like the other crew members, he was a former Navy flier. At the University of Texas where he met his wife Sue, he received a degree in aeronautical engineering. He received his first professional recognition at NASA through an unsought assignment. When astronauts Elliot See and Charles Bassett were killed in St. Louis after crashing into a building near the fog-bound airport, Bean was named to a prominent position in the six-man investigative board. The thoroughness of his investigation led to an impressively logical reconstruction of the accident which claimed the lives of two of his colleagues and friends.

A special burden fell on the Apollo 12 crew that had never before existed. All previous Apollo flights had been obvious stepping-stones to the moon landing. (Consequently, with each cumulative success, morale became even more stratospheric.) Low morale among NASA and contractor personnel had never been a problem, even after the disastrous Apollo fire. But in the fall of 1969 when the all-Navy crew arrived at the Kennedy Space Center for pre-launch rehearsals, morale in the space program had reached an all-time low. Budget cutbacks, and rumors of more cutbacks to come, combined with the general feeling of psychological letdown following mankind's "giant leap" in Apollo 11, contributed to a prevailing mood of lethargy. Visible evidence of the reduction in forces was reflected in the change from three shifts to two on the Apollo 12 pad and the substitution of a five-day work week for the normal seven days during pre-launch tests. Some NASA administrators privately expressed the fear that the negative mood was serious enough to cause space workers to become error prone. Some felt this human tendency might make Apollo 12 an even more dangerous journey than Apollo 11.

But the decline in morale did not apply in any way to the crew, especially to Alan Bean, who was getting his first space flight. As crew members went about final preparations, they looked forward, among other things, to the first scheduled color television from the moon.

Launch day, November 14, 1969, dawned amid darkening skies. Many outdoor spectators, including Vice

President Spiro Agnew, wore raincoats or carried umbrellas. At thirty-eight minutes to launch, NASA commentator Jack King reported the weather situation was still "touch and go." As launch time inched closer, the pad was nearly obscured by the mists shredding down from glowering skies. The giant rocket looked like a spectral ghost against a dark curtain backdrop. In the over fifty rocket launches I had witnessed, I had never seen one go — manned or unmanned — in weather that looked this bad. Incredibly, NASA allowed the countdown to continue even though a dense, black storm cloud appeared to hover directly above the pad during the final minutes.

The flame of ignition erupted like an artillery shell going off at night. The rocket rose, then with that ominous feeling that comes as one watches a giant jetliner disappear into the overcast before its wheels have fully retracted, I observed as Apollo 12 — just nine seconds after liftoff — was swallowed by the dark storm cloud.

Witnesses and a few movie cameras confirmed later that within thirty-seven seconds from liftoff, lightning flashed inside the cloud. One camera showed what appeared to be a vertical bolt following the wake of ionized gases pouring out the rocket's tail.

Aboard the Apollo 12, instruments suddenly showed a state of affairs so alarming and overwhelming that no one had ever been bold enough to crank it into a simulator. As the number one and two main electrical busses went out, indicating a power overload, alarm signals lighted up the cockpit panel like a Christmas tree.

"I don't know what happened here," Pete Conrad said,

when he could catch his breath. "We had everything in the world drop out. I think she must have been hit by lightning . . . We had so many lights on we couldn't read them all."

"We've had a couple of cardiac arrests down here too, Pete," Mission Control advised.

"We didn't have time for that up here," Pete responded with a nervous laugh.

Apollo 12 had, indeed, become the first known rocket main stage to have been struck by lightning. Fortunately, the sudden electrical overload immediately tripped by-pass circuits — something like household fuses — and lasting damage to delicate instruments was apparently prevented. Within a few seconds, everything except the main guidance system came back to normal. The crew switched instantly to the backup guidance system in time for the firing of the third stage. The firing went well. After a frightening beginning, all instruments finally read normally. As heart rates settled back to normal, every system in Apollo 12 was checked and double-checked. Nothing appeared to have been damaged.

"Well, I'll tell you one thing," said Conrad. "It's a first-class ride, Houston."

"You've got a go orbit. You're looking good," the ground responded as Mission Control settled down to proceed with the mission.

As the time for commitment to the moon neared, the ground advised, "The good word is you are go for TLI."

"Hoop-de-doo," crowed Pete Conrad. "We're ready. We didn't expect anything else."

The TLI burn and LEM docking went precisely as

planned. Then, the next burn placed Apollo 12 on a new and untried trajectory to the moon. All previous flights had followed a "loop-around" trajectory; that is, if nothing occurred to alter their course, they would circle the moon and return to earth without any additional burns. Now, however, the crew initiated a burn that took them out of the "free return" path and allowed them to proceed more directly toward their point of lunar orbit insertion. This meant that should any malfunction occur to cancel the mission, they could only return to earth by attempting another burn.

As the crew settled into the long coasting flight, Conrad advised jubilantly, "We're trying all those things we didn't have in Gemini, like toothpaste and shaving. We're really on the ball up here."

"Roger," Mission Control replied. "All dressed up and no place to go."

"Oh, we're going some place. We can see it. It gets bigger all the time."

On November 17, as they drew close to the moon, *Yankee Clipper* advised, "Our motion to the left is not as apparent as our motion toward the moon, and, therefore, we have the decided impression that we're going right into the center of that baby right now."

*Yankee Clipper* passed into the lunar darkness, got a go for LOI and passed behind the moon to initiate the crucial LOI burn.

After the scheduled behind-the-moon-time communications blackout — an interval that never got any shorter — Pete announced, "Hello, Houston. *Yankee Clipper* with *Intrepid* in tow has arrived on time. I guess like everybody else that just arrived, we are all here plastered to the windows, looking."

The next day, after two successful TV transmissions, Conrad and Bean entered the *Intrepid*, while Gordon remained alone in *Yankee Clipper*. Then the two craft separated. On the moon's far side, *Intrepid* began the burn that would take it down to 50,000 feet. At this point, *Intrepid*'s main descent engine fired up.

"I have ignition," Conrad reported. And *Intrepid* started down.

At 19,000 feet, Pete said, "I've got some kind of horizon out there. I've got some craters, too, but I don't know where I am yet . . . I'm trying to cheat and look out there. I think I see my crater."

Suddenly Alan Bean came on excitedly. "Pete, there it is. There it is! Son of a gun! Right down the middle of the road! Outstanding. Forty-two degrees, Pete."

"Hey," Pete said, "we're started right for the center of the crater. Look out there! I can't believe it. Amazing! Fantastic! Forty-two degrees, babe. Just keep talking."

BEAN: Coming down at ninety-nine feet a second. You're looking good.

HOUSTON: *Intrepid*, go for landing.

BEAN: Forty degrees, Pete.

CONRAD: Looks good out there, babe. Looks good . . . The boys on the ground do okay . . . Oh, look at that crater. Right where it's supposed to be. You're beautiful.

BEAN: You're looking good. Fifty feet coming down. Watch for the dust . . . Pete, you got plenty of gas, plenty of gas, babe. Stay in there.

HOUSTON: Thirty seconds.

BEAN: He's got it made. Come on in there . . . contact light.

CONRAD: Hey! Outstanding, man, beautiful! Man, oh man, I tell you, I think we're in a place a lot dustier than Neil's.

Pete Conrad had landed blind in a great cloud of black dust. His pulse rate read out in Houston at 129 beats per minute (compared to 140 when lightning struck). Although the *Intrepid* crew could not yet see Surveyor 3, Dick Gordon in *Clipper*, on his first pass overhead, created astonishment when he radioed, "I have *Intrepid*. I have *Intrepid* . . . He is on the Surveyor crater about a fourth of a Surveyor crater diameter to the northwest . . . Surveyor! I see Surveyor!"

Houston replied, "Roger, *Clipper*. Good eyeball. Well done."

Apollo 12 was to have no location problem, and now all attention turned toward the first walk on the surface. "I can't wait to get out there," Conrad and Bean both said at different moments during their preparations.

Conrad climbed out first. When he stepped down on the moon his comment was as humorous as Neil Armstrong's had been symbolically serious.

"Whoopie, man," the five-foot-six commander said, "that may have been a small one for Neil, but it was a long one for me."

Then he commented to Alan Bean, "You'll never believe it. Look what I see sitting on the side of the crater. Surveyor . . . Does that look neat. It can't be any further than six hundred feet from here. How about that?"

Now, Conrad tried out his moon legs. "It seems a little weird . . . Al, don't think you're going to steam around here quite as fast as you thought you were . . . You could work out here all day. Take your time . . . Hum de dump, dump, dump."

Occasionally humming or singing, both of them in a spirit of high glee, the two lunarnauts worked to set up the color TV. But, in the only failure of the mission, just as the TV picture came on in the MSC auditorium, we caught a flash of yellow and green and the tube went blank — apparently from the overbright light of the sun reflecting off *Intrepid*'s garish flanks.

With both stage screens dark, we were transported back to the old days of radio and visual imagination as the two men collected their quick "contingency" samples, then put up the flag.

"Okay," Conrad said, "we have the flag up. Like I say, hope everybody down there is as proud as we are to put it up."

Next, they unloaded the nuclear-powered ALSEP package, an improved and extended collection of scientific instruments to be left on the moon. Before the flight, referring to the ALSEP package and their lunar geological survey, Conrad had said, "The name of the game in Apollo 12 is lunar surface exploration. Let's face it. Anything we got scientifically off Apollo 11 was a bonus."

As they worked, amid frequent "dum de do, do, does" from Conrad, their casual words brought a distant world into the eye of the mind.

ALSEP is an acronym for Apollo Lunar Surface Experiments Package. Piece by piece, they reported the assembly of the $25 million remote observation station.

"Okay, I've got the solar wind deployed here," reported Conrad.

The solar wind experiment would measure the major atomic particles thrown off by the sun. The ion detector would measure the moon's tenuous atmosphere. The magnetometer would measure the unexpected strength of the moon's magnetic field, twenty to thirty times stronger than scientists had suspected. The seismometer would extend the Apollo 11 data on the physical properties of the moon's crust and interior. And the central data station would collect all the data and measurements and transmit them to earth. The power source for all this was a nuclear generator, painted bright red — not because it emitted dangerous rays but because, once armed, it would operate redhot. The nuclear furnace stood about one and a half feet high and on earth would weigh forty-four pounds. Its well-insulated capsule of nuclear fuel contained plutonium 238. As the plutonium spontaneously decayed radiation, it produced heat which was converted into enough steady electrical power to run the experiments. The biggest advantage of the nuclear power unit was its ability to function during the two-weeks-long lunar night. The Apollo 11 experiments had been powered by solar cells which, of course, need sunlight to function and were inoperative during the long lunar nights.

After the package was completely deployed, Conrad and Bean began their detailed collection of lunar rock samples. They had had nearly enough geology training to qualify them for an advanced geology degree, but from the comments we heard via radio, they sounded more like two boys exploring a lost gold mine.

"Oh, Al, there's a good rock," Conrad said at one point. "Look at this. Perfect. Perfect. We gotta have this . . . Dump de dum, dum."

"Hustle, boy, hustle," said Conrad once. "We got a lot of work to do."

They started to drive a core tube into the surface to collect soil samples at various depths.

"Okay," Bean reported. "I'm core tubing it right now."

"Auger it a bit," Conrad advised, "then pound it."

Finally, after they had spent nearly four hours on the moon, Houston advised them to get back in and rest up for their next excursion.

"We're going to have to smoke to get back there to LEM," Conrad said. "We're a long way."

"Pete and Al," Houston advised a few moments later, "we're picking up your heavy footsteps going by the seismometer."

"Okay, and then we gotta dust each other off and get in. Man, are we filthy . . . I tell you one thing. We're going to be a coupla dirty boogers. Man, did I get dirt all over myself. This is what is known as dirt, dirt, dirt."

After renewing their vital contact with Dick Gordon overhead, Conrad and Bean settled down for what rest and sleep they could manage in *Intrepid*'s spartan interior. Twelve and a half hours later, they emerged for their second excursion on the moon's surface having as main goals visits to surrounding craters and Surveyor 3.

First they readied their tools and equipment, then Conrad announced to Bean, "I'll lope off to ALSEP and check the sites. I'll meet you at twenty-one at Head Crater."

After verifying that ALSEP instruments were working, they made a painstaking geological traverse of about a mile, taking samples from six craters.

"There you go," Conrad said to Bean. "That's a good rock."

"Hey," Bean replied, "look at the pits in it, too."

"This is going to be a good rock, Houston, a real grapefruit," Conrad said as he put it in his sample bag. "Boy, there's some big fragments down here at Beach Crater. What a fantastic sight!"

At one point, Conrad asked his companion to halt. "Better we stop here and look at the chart a little bit. We're bushed."

Replied Bean, "Okay. Man does that LEM look small back there."

"Pete and Al," said Houston in a near miracle of long-range data interpretation, "We show you're twelve hundred feet from the LEM."

"Okay," Conrad replied, "You know what I feel like, Al?"

"What?"

"You ever see those pictures of giraffes running in slow motion? That's exactly what I feel like."

"Okay, I've got the decided feeling I'm going to sleep tonight."

When they arrived at the automatic robot, Surveyor 3, Conrad took hold of the spider-like craft that had been sitting on the moon for over two years. Strangely, it was covered with dust.

"Okay, Houston. I'm jiggling it. The Surveyor is firmly planted here. That's no problem."

Said Bean, "See the way the footpads dug in over here — dug up dirt."

For several minutes they worked to remove Surveyor's TV camera, sawing easily through the camera support tubes.

"In the bag. In the bag," Bean announced. "Pete, how about letting me cut this scoop off?"

"Sure," Pete said. "You didn't think we were going to leave without a scoop, did you?"

After they took pictures and left Surveyor, they stopped briefly at a crater called Block, and then proceeded back to *Intrepid* to stow the rock boxes. Bean went up to the porch while Conrad used a transfer apparatus similar to a clothesline reel to hoist the samples up to him. Finally, Pete said, "Okay, Houston, if you can mark me off the lunar surface."

"Roger," Houston replied. "We got that, Pete. At three hours and fifty minutes into the EVA."

"Hey, up the ladder I go. High ho. High ho. High ho." Everyone on the ground knew the sender of that tender message.

After sealing the hatch and hastening preparations for liftoff, the crew fired the ascent engine on schedule.

As *Intrepid* rose and moved to intercept *Yankee Clipper*, Gordon radioed, "Boy, you sure looked strange down there among all the sand dunes."

After linkup, Gordon told them, "You're home free, boys."

After crew transfer back to *Clipper*, they sent *Intrepid* on a deliberate crash course toward the moon's surface to help calibrate the seismometer left there. The crash was intended to produce an impact equivalent to the explosion of eight and a half tons of TNT. Houston flight controllers counted down for the lunar impact and then were startled when the seismometer registered strange lunar movements and reverberations for over half an hour after the crash.

"It was," said one expert, "as if one had struck a bell, say, in the belfry of a church, a single blow and found that the reverberations continued for thirty minutes."

Actually, the inexplicable reverberations were still measurable for fifty-five full minutes. The astonishing and unexpected results opened up an entire new chapter of speculation about the nature of the lunar interior. The amazing LEM-bug had added a highly significant data point to its outstanding service record. Like a good sacrifice fly, its last arcing flight may have brought in the most important run of all.

After orbiting the moon long enough to take the vital approach pictures of the ancient lunar mountains in the Fra Mauro highlands — intended landing site for Apollo 13 — *Yankee Clipper* performed its transearth injection burn.

"Hello, Houston," *Clipper* announced as it came out from behind the moon, "Apollo 12 is moving home."

But the long flight back was not to be entirely the un-

*Conrad and Bean inspect Surveyor 3*

eventful sleep-eat cycles of previous missions. Shortly before reentry, the crew and its busy cameras had an unprecedented and spectacular view. The crew members of Apollo 12 became the only human beings ever to see an eclipse of the sun by the earth.

"This has got to be the most spectacular view of the whole flight," Bean exclaimed, as the earth completely blotted out the mighty sun. "You can't see the earth. It's black just like the space."

Using smoked glasses, Conrad meticulously described subtleties of waning and waxing color bands that not even the most sensitive film could record.

At the end of its journey of scientific surprises, *Yankee Clipper* plopped into the choppy Pacific just thirteen seconds off the original schedule. The entire flight had lasted ten days, four hours and thirty-six minutes — from liftoff and lightning bolt to parachute drop 2.6 miles from the bow of the carrier *Hornet*.

There was one last moment of anxiety that temporarily brought back memories of the tragedy on pad 34. While riding the swells, Apollo 12 suddenly seemed to be afire as a smokelike substance flared up from the floating cone. But it was only Conrad venting extra fuel to lighten the lifting load of the spacecraft.

When helicopters deposited the crew safely on deck, Conrad, Bean and Gordon were directed inside the same mobile quarantine van that had been the temporary home of Armstrong, Aldrin and Collins. Since they had landed on a different part of the moon — several hundred miles from Tranquility Base — NASA administrators were again unwilling to chance the possible contamination of earth by unknown lunar substances.

Like their predecessors, the crew was booked for a twenty-one-day stay in quarantine in Houston's Lunar Receiving Laboratory. The monotony of their stay was relieved, however, by the aura of scientific excitement that surrounded their planned and unanticipated discoveries. As the next chapter indicates, we now knew enough about the moon — if not to settle its timeless mystery — at last to begin to construct a growing body of theory on the nature of some of its long imprisoned secrets.

As one intrigued scientist put it, "After Apollo 12, we're going to have to throw the book away and begin over again."

As we shall see, the moon was turning out to be far from a simple place.

## 12

# What We Are Learning from the Moon

*The most beautiful thing we can experience is the mysterious. It is the source of all true art and science. He to whom this emotion is a stranger, who can no longer rise to wonder and stand rapt in awe, is as good as dead; his eyes are closed.*
— ALBERT EINSTEIN, *The Forum*, October 1930

THE FASCINATING INFORMATION the Apollo flights brought back from our nearest neighbor in space was from five principal sources: the lunar rock and soil samples brought back to earth, the automatic scientific equipment in Apollo and the equipment left on the moon's surface, the still and motion pictures taken on or above the surface, the parts of Surveyor 3 retrieved by the Apollo 12 crew, and the experiences and physiological effects of the human explorers who made the journeys.

When the Apollo 11 explorers and rock samples first went into quarantine in Houston, the two most compelling questions were: does the moon contain anything that could contaminate man or earth? And what do the rocks and soil samples tell us about the moon's origin and evolution?

The answers to both these questions were considered so imperative by the public and press that investigative scientists — who normally are reluctant to advance theories based on preliminary findings — abandoned the usual scientific caution and succumbed to the temptation to match virtually every new fact with a new theory. It was several months, in fact, before the initial confusion and excitement abated to the point where reasonable men found the reflective time and required privacy to separate fact from opinion and to support theories based on a logical foundation that merged new data with old.

It was not unanticipated that there would be a certain amount of scientific "jumping the gun," and many thoughtful scientists resented the glare of publicity that greeted the investigation of the lunar soil samples. Some highly qualified individuals and institutions had been preparing for the analysis process for over two years. In an unprecedented procedure, NASA had made elaborate arrangements to parcel out fragments of the moon to 142 previously designated investigators in the United States and in foreign countries. For weeks, the carefully assembled scientific team at the Lunar Receiving Laboratory, who would get "first look" at the lunar payload, had practiced and rehearsed its procedures. Simulated-vacuum-packed boxes of lunar rocks were placed in an outside vacuum bathed in ultraviolet light, then cleaned with acid. The boxes were then opened in a vacuum as investigators using remote-control equipment and arm-length rubber gloves simulated the examination and chemical and physical analysis of the contents. Even those of us in journalism went through a trial run in covering the news the incoming rocks might reveal. No minerals in history had a comparable dollar value per gram of weight. One man estimated that the first expected boxes represented some $24 billion of space effort. Military police even practiced their security precautions and responsible role in protection of the priceless stones and dirt. Never before had such detailed preparations been made to examine and interpret a substance alien to earth. The reason, of course, was obvious, as the laboratory director, Dr. Persa Raymond Bell, explained to me before the manned lunar flights.

"Think what this means!" he pointed out. "We've never really had a preserved fragment from space. Meteors reaching us have all been distorted by heat. But the rocks brought back by the astronauts will be packed in a vacuum much like that found on the moon. Who knows what we will see when we open the boxes?"

The first two boxes of twenty pounds and thirty-nine pounds of lunar material were even flown to Houston in separate airplanes to lessen the chance that a possible accident would destroy what had taken man so long to obtain.

The first look at the samples on Saturday, July 26, 1969, was not quite the thrill Dr. Bell had anticipated. As the lid to the first treasure chest came off, scientists peered eagerly through portholes. Instead of seeing rocks and minerals they had been trained to identify, they first saw what looked something like gray peat or powdered charcoal. All the rocks were covered with an opaque, fine-grained, dark-colored dust.

"I've never been so frustrated in my life," said the laboratory curator Dr. Elbert King. "There was not a single mineral I could identify. Being a mineralogist I find this somewhat embarrassing."

His disappointment was understandable, but it was partly relieved as the rocks themselves were lifted out and cleaned of their shroud of clinging particles. One man described a lumpy rock as looking like an Idaho potato that had fallen through the grate into a bed of ashes. The mysterious dust turned out to be medium gray in color with a slight brownish cast under certain lighting conditions.

The second surprise was the abundance of pebblelike glassy-looking material with remarkably high luster that ranged in color from dark brown and amber to yellow and clear. Some of the glassy spheroids, or vesicles, glinted out of the gray lunar rocks like tiny diamonds.

During the next few days, bits of lunar dust were placed under the skin of mice and in oysters and other life forms to test for unknown, or possibly harmful, organic substances. None were identified. Preliminary tests showed the presence of such minute amounts of organic material that they could easily have come from handling tools the astronauts used. No organic material either living or fossilized could be found under a 300,000-power microscope.

The second box of samples contained rocks with sharper angles than those in the first box; twelve of the

rocks were bigger than golf balls. One of the first investigators to report was Dr. Oliver Schaeffer of New York
University, who found in the dust samples he melted
down an unexpectedly large amount of gases, such as hydrogen and helium, that he felt had definitely come from
the sun. The gases escaped and were analyzed when he
heated a pinch of lunar dust to 3,000 degrees Fahrenheit.
Such gaseous material from the sun could not penetrate
to the earth because of our atmosphere. He speculated
that the solar wind could have created the dust by erod-
ing and flaking the lunar surface. Dr. Schaeffer also
found surprising amounts of such gases as argon, neon,
krypton and zenon.

The presence of so much glass embedded in the rocks
led to the almost immediate conclusion by many that the
rocks were igneous, or heat-formed, and some young geologists announced privately that this already proved Dr.
Harold Urey wrong. Urey had long believed that the
moon was essentially "cold" and had never had a molten
core like that of the earth. But when the rock samples
were more thoroughly dated, they turned out to be so
unexpectedly old — an estimated 3.1 billion years, instead of several hundred million years as many young geologists believed — that Urey's cold moon theory took
on a possible new validity.* If the igneous rocks were
that old, speculation now ran, they could have been
formed near the time of the birth of the solar system and

---

* Dr. Gerald J. Wasserburg of the California Institute of Technology
in April 1970 estimated from his study of lunar rocks that the moon
was at least 3.4 billion years old and had a period of sustained tur-
bulence about a billion years after its formation.

could have remained virtually unchanged since very early in the moon's formation. This could mean that the relatively new maria had not seen a possible lava outflow for billions of years; otherwise the heat-formed surface rocks would have been covered up by the escaping molten interior. Poor old Harold Urey, as some had referred to him, might be largely right after all.

The dating process first used was known as potassium-argon dating. Since it takes 1.3 billion years for radioactive potassium to decay at a predictable rate into argon, the ratio of potassium to argon in a given sample helps in the age estimation process.

Other quick conclusions also proved erroneous. At first, some geologists had announced that the moon and earth seemed to be rather similar in structure and evolution and that the moon was made up of earthlike layers, but the discovered presence of large amounts of titanium, comparatively rare on earth, and the infrequent faint lunar rumbles detected by the seismometer now did not point to a moon that was as geologically stratified and "alive" as is the earth.

Dr. Schaeffer's discovery of solar argon in the surface of the moon rocks also indicated that there had been no relatively recent upheavals on the moon, at least in the area of Tranquility Base.

The bulk of the Apollo 11 findings and the increasing possibility that the molten lava in the marias may have been caused by violent meteor impact seemed, at first, to take some of the wind out of those who had expounded two theories of the moon's nature: that it was actively volcanic in relatively recent years and that it was once torn out of the side of a hot earth. The cold moon theory, however, did not so far destroy either of the other two theories of the moon's origin: that it was formed from scattered dust, gases and debris whirling around the earth or that it was captured by the earth's gravity.

As the weeks passed, scientists grew noticeably more cautious in attempting to explain the enigma of the moon. But in October, a startling new theory was put forth by a highly responsible astronomer, Dr. Thomas Gold of Cornell University. His theory grew out of Neil Armstrong's visual observation of glassy patches that glittered like broken bottles in the bottoms of about seven craters. This "glazing" led Gold to the theory that the moon may have been temporarily and fairly recently heated, or scorched, by a violent flareup from the sun, possibly due to a collision with a large comet. The violence of the fiery outburst Gold estimated at one hundred times the normal power of the sun; the brilliant conflagration could have been very brief. The craters, he speculated, would have been natural heat traps if such an event had occurred, and, unless the event occurred fairly recently, the melting and glazing in the saucer-shaped heat traps would have been obliterated by the constant bombardment of meteorites and solar particles. If this possibility checks out with additional Apollo flights, it could mean that Mercury, the closest planet to the sun, might be seared on one entire side.

Another theory advanced prior to the Apollo 12 flight included speculation that the moon may be like a great, shattered brittle ball beneath its crust, with fissures and cracks penetrating deep into the moon's interior. Speculation also mounted on the nature of the lunar mascons, the strange mass concentrations that caused the moon to exert an uneven gravitational pull on orbiting bodies. Were they embedded iron meteors? Or the maria themselves? The lunar dust was later found to be half glass, not one-third as at first believed. This, some speculated, could account for the slippery nature of the surface Armstrong and Aldrin had discovered. Stereoscopic photographs they brought back suggested they were walking on thin crusts of dark glass.

The surprisingly abundant glass, the great store of harmless radioactivity in the rocks, the high density of the rocks compared to the rest of the lunar surface, the surprising age of the lunar surface, all suggested to Columbia University's Dr. Paul Gast that the moon had "an evolutionary history very different from that of earth's." The seismometer, especially, continued to show very faint signals completely different from any earth movement activity recorded by seismometers on our still active planet. The so-called "unlayered theory" appeared to be gaining ground.

In the midst of all this intense speculation one scientist — to the dismay of children all over the world — even seriously pointed out that the illusion of a "man on the moon" was merely a "reflective variation of the albedo* on different parts of the moon."

When I finally saw my first moon rocks, I had to step

---

* albedo — "Astron. The ratio of the light reflected by a planet or satellite to that received by it." Random House Dictionary of the English Language.

between two armed military policemen to peer down at a lemon-sized angular rock glittering with jeweled fragments of glass. The base rock itself looked like gray charcoal. A man near me said that if he ran across it in a parking lot, he wouldn't have bothered to pick it up. But I would have. I would have been instantly intrigued by the shining fragments that peered out at me, almost as if alive, like the bright, dark eyes of rodents.

On November 26, 1969, the first two boxes of Apollo 12 lunar material arrived at the lunar laboratory under a twenty-five-man guard after a nonstop flight from Pago Pago in the Pacific. The first impression of scientists was that the new moon rocks were not much different from the Tranquility samples, but closer inspection later showed intriguing differences. One of the first rocks looked at was the one Pete Conrad had called a "grapefruit"; it was about the size of a softball. It weighed 3.66 pounds compared to the 2.1 pounds of the largest rock in the Apollo 11 collection.

But other differences proved to be of more interest to science than a mere disparity in size. In Apollo 12's cargo scientists could find no rocks, called breccia, which showed signs of having been welded together by some heat or shock process. Yet such rocks were part of the Apollo 11 treasure trove. The dust in Apollo 12 also appeared finer. The titanium percentage was also surprisingly lower. The new rocks also contained larger crystals — one that was an inch thick — and were more coarse grained. The most significant difference, however, was in the report that the Apollo 12 rocks were thought to be a billion years younger than those taken from Tranquility

Base, some eight hundred miles away. As in the earlier rock samples, no signs of bacterial activity or toxicity were found in any of the rocks.

The cool moon theory received a slight shakeup on December 27 when my friend Dr. Robin Brett reported some evidence of the moon's volcanic past. He announced that one of the core tubes he had analyzed had light and dark layers in it, and that one of the layers appeared to be volcanic ash.

"The dust is different," he said, "and we don't understand why yet."

It was not until thirty-five days after the first Apollo 12 rocks arrived that more detailed comparisons and findings could be generally interpreted. This was done on the occasion of a four-day meeting in Houston of a symposium of the 142 lunar material investigators. Over 1,100 scientists from around the globe assembled in the Albert Thomas Convention Center to hear the reports.

The first surprise was that the Apollo 11 rocks, under a complicated uranium dating process, turned out to be even older than had been earlier supposed from potassium dating. They were estimated to be — not 3.1 billion years — but 4.6 billion years old, about as old as many scientists believe the earth to be.

University of Chicago's mineralogist Dr. J. V. Smith also announced his theory that the moon's core was now solid but that it had once been molten. The presence of the broad maria on the front side compared to their virtual absence on the back side, he thought, was due to the fact that the earth's gravitation drew the last liquid magma, rich in heavy iron and titanium, to one side through breaks in the crust. Smith described some of the glass spheroids as they appeared under electron microscopes as similar to golf balls covered with dimples.

The world's first lunar science conference also revealed several new minerals, including tranquilite, something like the earth mineral pseudobrookite; kennedyite (which has no relationship to John F. Kennedy); and pyroxmangite, an iron analogue which is not found anywhere on earth. Investigators had also discovered the presence of small amounts of gold and silver and some fragments of rubies. Dr. Robert Walker of Washington University reported a mysterious lunar erosion process that wore away approximately four-hundredths of an inch of surface material every million years. The same mysterious process, Dr. Thomas Gold speculated, must have filled in the trenches initially left by the small rock fragments violently thrown out by impact or volcanism, perhaps hundreds of miles across the lunar surface.

"Otherwise," asked Dr. Gold, "what happened to the trenches the rocks would have dug?" This recalled another mystery: why the Surveyor 3 lunar probe was covered with dust when the tops of nearby exposed rocks billions of years old were free of dust. What was moving the dust around on the moon? And how?

One of the most distinguished delegates to the conference, famed British astrophysicist Dr. Fred Hoyle, commented on the scientific transformation taking place: "I predicted in 1948 that once pictures of the earth as seen from the outside became available, all sorts of new ideas would be let loose . . . You see now how concerned everyone has become to help protect the natural environment. All the natural scientists have been saying this is important for a long time . . . Now something new is happening to make us aware that earth is a precious place . . . From now on space exploration will have to work alongside terrestrial laboratories as the mainsprings of discovery. We're seeing that today as we struggle to understand the moon."

At a time when new questions mounted faster than old questions could be answered, when old theories turned over in their graves and new theories sprang up like spring flowers, the separation of reasonable fact from tempting speculation was not always easy. As Apollo flights continue, as they must, these findings, in summary, indicate some of the more important things we must learn about our only natural satellite.

The moon has at least four basic rock types: lunar soil composed of a variety of glasses and mixed with crystal and angular rock fragments; fine-grained crystalline rocks filled with bubbles which formed when the rocks were molten; coarser-grained rocks filled with irregular cavities which formed when the rocks were partly molten;and breccia material made up of chunks of once molten rock embedded in compacted, or impact-hardened, lunar soil. The source of the heat that formed the igneous rocks is essentially unknown. It is reasonably certain that something hot and violent occurred on the moon after it was formed. The moon is not layered like earth, nor does its surface composition resemble that of earth. Carbon composition, for instance, one of the earth's most identifiable characteristics, has formed differently on the moon. An analysis of six moon rocks shows, however, that they are similar to the basalt rocks found at the mid-ocean ridges on the bottom of earth's seas.

The age of the moon, of course, is very great and those who, prior to the Apollo flights, had thought of the moon as a visible and essential record of the solar system's past were essentially correct. Not wind, not rain, not ice, nothing save the fall of large and small meteorites and the solar wind had violated the moon's surface integrity for billions of years. Nothing, that is, unless it were a stray comet which somehow ignored the powerful magnet of the earth for the lesser gravity of the moon. The lunar dust, in fact, is the oldest material man has ever found.

The nature of the moon's interior is still essentially unknown after the first manned lunar landings. Life as we know it has probably never existed on the moon. And this, from a scientific standpoint, is perhaps fortunate; now we have the chance to compare a totally lifeless world to a world rich in life. There are no fossils found, no water, no bacteria, no germs. If water ever existed on the moon, it probably has been lost in the violent cauldron of white hot heat. Those tiny, high-velocity space bullets, micrometeorites, have peppered and eroded virtually every square inch of the moon's surface. Even tiny glass globules show indentations. The moon, as one scientist described it, is a continuous "cosmic battlefield." In addition to evidence of heat, there is evidence of shock.

"It seems to me," says Dr. Robert Jastrow, "that the old description in terms of the hot and cold moon is now

*The moon is won*

clearly an oversimplification and that a richer and more varied set of circumstances is involved in the early history of the moon."

One of the most significant of all discoveries was that all moon rocks — despite their strangeness when analyzed in earth laboratories — are similar in terms of chemistry to earth rocks, and this fact points to a general family relationship. As Dr. John Maxwell puts it, "It's the same alphabet but a different grammar." This family relationship strongly supports a certain universality of the natural laws of the cosmos. The earth and moon exist jointly according to the fundamental laws of nature. No Devil has made the moon. Ancient man and all the dreamers and poets down through the ages would have been pleased to know that.

# Index